The story of Shirley

M. Sawbridge (Editor)

British Textile Technology Group, Shirley Towers, Wilmslow Road, Didsbury, Manchester M20 8RX, UK, 1988, 85 pages. Price £8.50 (plus packing and postage). ISBN 0-903669-48-X. In English.

This is basically a work for the general reader and marks the passing of the name 'Shirley Institute' following the formation of the British Textile Technology Group. It traces the development of the Institute from a local research centre into one having an international reputation. Chapters deal with the first fifty years from 1919, the 1970s and the 1980s. The work of the Institute is examined in another chapter. Present and past working and social conventions and attitudes are also discussed. Three appendices contain bibliographical information.

[B] 1989/714

D1649177

The Story of Shirley

155873

Certificate of Incorporation

I Hereby Certify, That the

British Cotton Industry Research Association
(the word Limited being omitted by Licence of
the Board of Trade)

is this day Incorporated under the Companies Acts, 1908 to 1917, and that the Company is Limited.

Given under my hand at London, this *Seventh* day of *June* One Thousand Nine Hundred and *Nineteen*.

Fees and Deed Stamps £ *22 =*

Stamp Duty on Capital £ *=*

H. Butler

Registrar of Joint Stock Companies.

Certificate of Incorporation of the British Cotton Industry Research Association.

The Story of Shirley

A history of Shirley Institute, Manchester, 1919-1988

Contributors:
L.H.C. Tippett, H.M. Taylor, M. Sawbridge,
R.J.E. Cumberbirch, A.J.G. Sagar.

Acknowledgement for photographs
Page 11 (upper), "Manchester Guardian"; p.22, Kemsley Newspapers; p.58, Shark Sports
Ltd; p.73, "Daily Express".

ISBN 0-903669-48-X
Edited by Maureen Sawbridge.
Typesetting by Minstrel, Sale, Cheshire.
Printed by BPCC Northern Printers Ltd, Blackpool, Lancs.
Published by Shirley Institute, Didsbury, Manchester M20 8RX.

Contents

Preface

The question most commonly asked by visitors to Shirley Institute was how did the organization come to be so named. The intriguing answer is at the very beginning of the story you are about to read. Shirley Institute is now part of the British Textile Technology Group (BTTG), the result of the long-awaited integration with our sister organization, Wira Technology Group, and like that organization we have a history in which we take considerable pride. The history to date is in two very distinct parts.

The first part takes us from the establishment of the Institute in 1919 as the Research Association for the British Cotton Industry, up to 1971 when the statutory levy, by which Shirley received a high proportion of its funds, was withdrawn. The senior appointment to the Association was always that of Director of Research, and this post was filled by a series of eminent men of science: Dr Crossley, Sir Robert Pickard, Dr Toy, and Dr Hill. The prime responsibility of these Directors was to ensure that the basic research felt necessary for the underpinning of the technology of the industry was carried out to standards which were exacting both technically and academically. Under their guidance, though "command" might be a more appropriate word, a distinctive Shirley Institute style was forged, to which this volume pays due homage. In these fifty years, the Directors were supported primarily by the UK Cotton Industry as a corporate body, and also by the Government of the day.

The second part of the story will be seen in the fullness of time as the transition phase between Research Association and self-supporting commercial entity. To Len Wiseman, still titled Director of Research, mainly fell the task, at times thankless, at times frustrating, at times disheartening, but in the end exciting and rewarding, of initiating this traumatic change of direction, and ensuring that, against very long odds, the Institute survived. It has been my privilege to see that second phase to completion, to the point where a sound financial basis for the Institute has been established and from which the British Textile Technology Group can operate with long-term confidence.

The story of Shirley is a story of its people, and each one of the many thousands who worked in the organization in the past seventy years has had some contribution to make to that story. It is simply not possible to do justice to the personal contributions of so many, nor to weight them sensibly to give full credit where credit is due. We apologize therefore to all those who may feel aggrieved that they have not been mentioned, and to those who judge that their input has not been adequately recognized; that apology is unreserved.

The Shirley style and impact on the textile industry is maybe best illustrated by a quotation from Sir Robert Pickard in the first volume of the "Shirley Institute Bulletin", the publication by which the Institute's findings were communicated to the industry – "It is one of the most outstanding lessons to be learnt from the history of industrial development that technical revolutions germinate from the scientific probing of plain accepted facts". There is no truck here with the ephemera of technological fashion: rather the clear indication that incremental improvement by disciplined science is more worthwhile and productive than the search for the headline-demanding breakthrough. What Shirley has achieved for the industry has come much more from patient, detailed application than from fundamental scientific advance.

Historic retrospection risks becoming nostalgia for an irrecoverable past, but that is not our intention. Since our new colleagues have set the fashion in the companion volume to this book, "The Story of Wira", for quoting from Churchill (the Sir Robert Pickard of British politics), why not follow suit? "The nation which forgets its own history has no future." It is to our future we now look as we set down our past. When I was a lad at school, one of the buildings was called the Pink School, although it was actually a rather faded mustard shade; this had been applied shortly after the First World War, but the local population refused to recognize the change of colour. I am sure the name of Shirley will live long, but I also hope without the refusal to recognize the real changes we will go through which the change in name to BTTG presages.

I cannot end this preface without taking a final risk in potentially causing offence. Many people have been involved in putting this book together, but I must especially thank Maureen Sawbridge, not just for her editing and cajoling efforts, but for chronicling the last eight years of our existence; H.M. Taylor (who may actually have Christian names but these are never disclosed in public) for reviewing the Wiseman years; Reg Cumberbirch and Anthony Sagar for their personal assessments of sociological changes in the workplace; and, strangely and posthumously, L.H.C. Tippett, whose review of the first fifty years of Shirley Institute's existence seemed such an appropriate foundation for this book, since in both style and technical eminence he embodied much of the Shirley tradition. May the best of it survive and be nurtured by BTTG.

Alasdair Maclean

Chapter I
The First Fifty Years

Introduction

During the first World War the Government and leaders of industry became seized of the thought that the military struggle would be succeeded by a struggle for commercial and industrial survival, and that hitherto British industry had not benefited from the application of science as much as it might have done. The Department of Scientific and Industrial Research (DSIR, later incorporated in the Ministry of Technology) was established with the duty, among others, of encouraging the formation of associations for cooperative research in industries. It had a fund of £1 million, to be used in furthering this object. The Lancashire cotton industry, as one of the country's most important industries, naturally received attention, and in 1916 a Provisional Committee of Research and Education for the Cotton Industry, consisting largely of leaders of the industry, was formed to consider what should be done.

The industry was at that time conscious of its strength and importance. The Provisional Committee boasted that Lancashire had 42% of the spinning spindles of the world, and the industry was commonly recognized as Britain's largest exporter. The Provisional Committee warned, however, that the industry could not rest on past achievements. Foreign competition would be vigorous and such natural advantages as Lancashire had were fast disappearing. All the aid that science could give would be required, and this would call for something new to be done because there had been little technical development since 1850. The Committee wisely did not promise that science would enable the industry to maintain its position in the world.

In 1919 the British Cotton Industry Research Association (BCIRA) was formed, and although it enjoyed financial help and encouragement from DSIR, it was run by the industry, which provided most of the money.

At first the BCIRA had rooms in Manchester University but in 1920 it acquired a 14½-acre estate and mansion, marked on Ordnance Survey maps as "The Towers", situated at Didsbury, about six miles on the south side of Manchester. Mr W. Greenwood, a spinner and member of the Provisional Committee, contributed handsomely to the purchase price and asked in return that his daughter, Shirley, should be commemorated by calling the place "Shirley Institute". Doubtless the fame of the Institute is due to the excellence of its work, but the name has helped the spread of that fame. In 1942 a further 4 acres of land was acquired adjacent to the original estate.

The original "Shirley" (Marian Shirley Greenwood), after whom the Institute was named.

A view of The Towers, Didsbury, Manchester, the house in which Shirley Institute began its work, and the first (1922) laboratories.

Opening of the laboratories by HRH the Duke of York on 28th March 1922.

The choice of site has proved to be very good. The surroundings are pleasant, living facilities for the staff are good in the area, and the place is easily accessible by road, rail and air.

The first laboratories were opened by the (then) Duke of York in 1922, and every few years after that an extension or new building was added until about 1936.

In 1936 the British Silk Research Association, which had been established at Leeds, came to Shirley Institute and formed a Silk Section. There was no change in the title of the BCIRA.

The 1920s saw the gradual introduction of viscose rayon as a new textile fibre which the Lancashire industry, more than any other textile industry, adopted, processing the fibre first on its existing "cotton" machines and later modifying them as experience proved this to be necessary. Shirley Institute, in serving the technical interests of its Members, built up a substantial body of research on the processing of rayon, to which the rayon producers gave financial support. During the second world war, the British Rayon Federation was set up as a trade body to bring together the interests of rayon producers, processors and primary distributors, and in considering what should be done about research the Federation decided to establish an independent research organization. This it did in full knowledge and appreciation of the work of Shirley Institute and other textile research associations, and after considering alternative ways of providing for research. At that time, people in the rayon-producing industry felt, sometimes passionately, that there was a danger of the progress of the new fibre being hampered by having its processing closely and exclusively dependent on the older textile industries based on the processing of natural fibres, and there were abroad ideas of the development of a separate man-made fibre processing industry with its own specially developed machines and methods. The establishment of a separate research organization was a natural expression of those ideas.

Hence, in 1946 the British Rayon Research Association (BRRA) was formed. It established its headquarters first, and as a temporary measure, in part of a factory in Trafford Park, and subsequently in new laboratories built at Heald Green (near Manchester International Airport and about four miles from Shirley Institute) and opened by the Duke of Edinburgh. Although based on and largely financed by the British Rayon Federation (except for a Government grant), BRRA was from the first intended to deal largely with the processing of rayon rather than with its production. In the early papers, rayon was the fibre mentioned, but quite soon it was understood that the Association would also serve the newer man-made fibres that were coming into use.

BRRA rapidly established itself and began to deal with the technical problems of processors. As time went on, however, the expected separation between the processing of cotton and man-made fibres failed to take place. Most of the firms that used rayon also used cotton, often in the same mills, and the advantages of blending fibres began to be realised, thus making separation even more difficult. Synthetic fibres appeared upon the scene, and these were processed by existing spinners, weavers, and finishers, and the technical problems were dealt with by existing organizations. Thus it came about that BCIRA and BRRA had a large common membership and did similar work. Indeed, sometimes a mill man sent the same problem to both organizations doubtless intending, if the two answers were different and some commercial dispute was involved, to use the one that better suited his purposes. There were rivalries as well as cooperation between members of the two staffs. In the late 1950s the view gained ground in the industry that there was undesirable overlap in the work being done. A joint committee considered this and as a result arrangements were made which were designed to improve cooperation between BCIRA and BRRA but they were not entirely successful. The Gordian knot was cut when, after consideration by a working party from the industry, the two associations were in 1961 amalgamated to form The Cotton Silk and Man-made Fibres Research Association (CSMFRA).

The inclusion of silk was for the first time, and when silk had almost ceased to be used as a fibre, signified in the title of the joint research organization. For administrative convenience the new body was formally a continuance of the BCIRA under a new name, but essentially it was a merger between equal parties. It was practically and financially convenient to establish the headquarters of the CSMFRA at the BCIRA premises at Didsbury, where additions were made to the buildings. Because of its prestige in the scientific and textile worlds, the title "Shirley Institute" was retained.

Dr A.W. Crossley, FRS, the first Director, 1920-27.

Sir Robert Pickard, FRS, Director, 1927-43.

Opening of the 1936 extensions by Lord Derby.

Early days of BCIRA

The Provisional Committee that led to the formation of BCIRA argued very strongly that the new organization should not only deal with the industry's immediate problems, but should do basic research into raw materials, processes, and products. This was argued with force and elegance of expression, and the report of the Provisional Committee makes good reading even after a lapse of time. Certainly the spirit behind the report has guided Shirley Institute from its earliest days and experience has proved the wisdom of what was written.

The choice of Director of Research was regarded as crucial, and in 1920 Dr A. W. Crossley, FRS, then professor of chemistry at King's College, London, was appointed. He recruited a scientific staff and established an organization in which departments were named by sciences: botany, physics, organic chemistry, inorganic chemistry, colloid physics, colloid chemistry. This list discloses the early approach to the Institute's work. The Library and Information Department was regarded as being very important, and there were service departments or sections.

The staff, being without knowledge or experience of the industry and its technology – a technology can scarcely be said to have existed – conducted such researches as their general scientific knowledge and experience dictated. In the Botany Department work was carried out on cotton plants of various types grown in a greenhouse at the Institute. Microscopical examination was made of the structure and development of the fibres during growth and the results, besides being of general interest, provided information on which were based tests for fibre maturity and for damage of various types – mechanical, chemical, and biological. Studies in genetics and cytology were also made but these were not carried very far because they became the province of the Empire Cotton Growing Corporation, later the Cotton Research Corporation. The department developed the methods of measuring the characteristics of cotton fibre which formed the basis for assessing cottons commercially.

The chemical departments laid the foundations for studies of the fabric-finishing processes by developing analytical methods, determining the chemical constituents of cotton, and studying the chemical and physical characteristics of the materials used in processing – notably starch. Quite early on, a fluidity test for the chemical degradation of cotton was established, and this has been the basis for control in bleaching by hypochlorite ever since, as well as having uses in other industries and connections. The process of warp sizing was studied and the beginnings were made with work that revolutionized that part of the industry.

Previous to 1920, physics had scarcely been applied to spinning and weaving: early work was exploratory and some of it led nowhere. Highly significant, however, were tests that were developed for measuring continuously the thickness of slivers, roving and yarns, as was the statistical analysis of the resulting series of figures. The importance of the form of the variation, particularly of the wave-like-form, became recognized and the foundations were laid for a later understanding of the causes of yarn variation.

The general science of physical testing provided a fruitful starting point for the physical testing of fibres, yarns, and fabrics, but special developments were necessary. Already-existing tests were rationalized (e.g. the effects of the rate of loading and the specimen length on strength were measured) and new tests, such as one for measuring the stiffness of fabrics, were developed. The importance of moisture on the properties of textiles had long been recognized, and definitive work was done on the moisture content of cotton (and later rayon) in equilibrium with atmospheres of different temperatures and relative humidities.

Although the Institute at first concentrated on the fundamentals of the industry's processes and materials, it did not take a remote attitude, and contact with the industry and its practical problems was encouraged. But the going was hard; scientists and technical managers had yet to learn to understand each other. Occasionally a mill would send a problem to the Institute, and this would be considered at a meeting of all the heads of department before being sent to the laboratories, a cumbersome procedure contrasting strongly with today's more streamlined practice.

Dr Crossley died early in 1927 while still in office and was succeeded by Dr R. H. (later Sir Robert) Pickard, FRS. During Dr Crossley's illness and before Dr Pickard took charge, there was no Director—an experience that showed the need for one.

Increasing contact with the industry

One of Sir Robert Pickard's first steps was to build up a sense of cohesion among the staff and a system of internal control, so that all technical information given out was that of the Shirley Institute personified by the Director. A "Shirley tradition" began to grow. This limited the freedom of the staff, but they were all made to feel that they contributed to the Institute's statements and that they shared responsibility for them. This contrasted with the previous situation in which Heads of Departments assumed considerable independence, and scientists within departments were subjected to a control that cabined and confined all but the strong-minded. As from the beginning, scientific papers continued to be published over the names of the staff who did the work, but most reports and papers confidential to the industry were anonymous. Internal meetings were instituted at which members of the staff described their work to their colleagues, so that every member had opportunity of knowing what was going on all over the Institute. These developments were welcomed by the staff—at least by those in the intermediate and lower reaches.

Sir Robert Pickard took vigorous steps to bring the Institute and the industry closer together, and to help the industry to apply the results of the research work. This was seen to be necessary if the industry was to continue to support the Institute, and hence if the Institute was to continue to existence. In 1928 he established a Liaison Department consisting of young textile technologists with industrial experience, whose main duty was to visit mills, learn of their technical problems, explain and apply the results of the Institute's work. These visits did much to influence the development of the research programme along practical lines.

In 1928 the first number of the "Shirley Institute Bulletin" appeared. Hitherto publications had been largely in the form of scientific papers published in the "Journal of the Textile Institute". These continued, but additionally the Bulletin was intended to present the technical results of research in a language the mill man could understand. The scientists had to learn how to do this, and the mill man had to acquaint himself with a few basic terms and ideas (e.g. fluidity, variation), and some years elapsed before complaints of the unintelligibility of the Bulletin largely ceased. To the Bulletin were added special pamphlets, covering particular topics, that were issued from time to time. Most of these were confidential to Member firms.

One result of these developments was that increasingly mills would send to the Institute their specific, immediate, technical problems. The submission would usually take the form of a piece of defective fabric or other material with a request to be informed of the cause of the defect, where it occurred, and whose fault it was. The Institute's avowed objective in providing this service was to show how to avoid the defect in future, but more often than not the report was used in the settlement of claims between processors. This "special case" service, as it was called, became very popular and has continued to provide one of the Institute's strongest contacts with the industry.

Another way of penetrating into the industry is to have people working in mills who have been trained at the Institute, and a start was made in this direction. Young men destined for higher management would spend several months at the Institute, and this has been repeated in various forms in later years, so that by now, with these people and ex-members of Shirley staff, hundreds of the industry's technical leaders have had an extended stay at the Institute. In addition, special training courses in particular subjects were given, and have continued from time to time all through the Institute's history, to technicians as well as technologists. The policy has been not to duplicate the work of the technical colleges but to augment their courses and fill gaps.

Work of the practical kind began to take a larger place in the Institute's programme, and the first expansion of buildings in this period made provision for extensive workrooms for spinning and weaving, well equipped with full-scale machinery. There was not enough space and money for more than a small range of finishing equipment. This situation was remedied considerably in 1963, and a further major finishing re-equipment scheme was completed about 1970.

From the beginning it was thought that one of the results of research would be the development of new processing methods and machines that could be patented. It has been said that in the optimistic first days the staff were encouraged to believe that before long their salaries would be doubled by

Views of the labs in the 1920s and 1930s.

the proceeds from royalties. A few items had early been patented and developed into machines – the Shirley Card, now defunct, is one – but only incidentally, as an offshoot of the research work, and the results were meagre. In the 1930s machinery development and commercial exploitation were more directly pursued. An Opening and Cleaning Department was formed to study the early processes of the spinning mill, and a large part of its efforts was devoted to the development of machines. The necessary engineering work was done at first by outside firms, but in spite of friendly cooperation this proved to be unsatisfactory, and the department was equipped with a substantial drawing office and machine shop. Though the first machines to be produced were not satisfactory in mill trials, after the War a number of successes were achieved. One such machine, the "Shirley" Analyser, became the internationally accepted standard for determining the percentage of impurities present in baled cotton. Another notable development was "Shirlan", a fungicide intended to prevent mildew in cotton goods stored under damp conditions, but also having wide-spread use in agriculture and horticulture.

During Sir Robert Pickard's time, although most of the research was done with practical ends directly in mind, and the proportion of applied, and even ad hoc, work increased, problems continued to be looked at fundamentally, and long-term basic work continued. One notable example was the laying of the foundations of cloth geometry. Another was the investigation of the structure of cellulose through studying the effects of treatment by acids, alkalis, and oxidizing agents.

The increasing volume of work on the processing of rayon led to the formation in 1927 of a Rayon Department which, with other departments of the Institute, did much to help the Industry over the early difficulties of using the new fibre. One substantial project was an investigation into the production of crepe fabrics.

The Second World War

During the War Shirley Institute came under the Essential Work Orders and the staff of about 200 were directed to remain where they were, except that three or four were released to work directly for Government Departments. Work continued substantially as before, but practical problems of immediate importance to the mills were attacked with an increased sense of urgency, and any arising from the War were given absolute priority. A few examples will show the kind of thing that was done.

Immediately after Dunkirk the army was short of khaki webbing and all the suitable looms in the country were put to work to supply the need. The Institute had four heads of such looms intended for experimental purposes, and over a few months these produced many miles of webbing, being worked day and night. Another service of the Weaving Department was the design of a fabric that could be used as a "de-lousing" belt. The idea was that when the belt was worn next to the skin by soldiers under unfavourable field conditions, lice would be attracted into puckers that had been designed into the fabric and could be burnt with the belt. No report was ever received of the usefulness of the device.

The ebb and flow of the war had its effect on the Institute's work. In the early days, before lease-lend from the USA, economies in the use of American cotton were necessary and the Institute had to help the industry to extend the use of Indian and Egyptian cotton. Later, when the Mediterranean became closed to British shipping, the Institute had to assist the substitution of American for Egyptian cotton. Experiments were made with the various substitute sizing materials that became available and had to be used instead of the usual sago, particularly when the War extended to the Far East. Flax was much used in canvases for water-holding military stores, and the cutting off of supplies from the Netherlands made it necessary to find a substitute. The Institute determined the conditions under which cotton could be made to satisfy the exacting requirements, and for a time a large water-holding dam made of uncoated cotton canvas was a feature of the Shirley landscape.

Other items directly connected with the War included work on the mildew-proofing and rot-proofing of textiles for use in the Far East; the sizing, weaving, and finishing of nylon, then a new fibre that was being used as a substitute for silk in parachute fabrics; the design and testing of black-out fabrics; the testing and appraisal of cotton yarn for the price-quality scheme of the Cotton Control; investigations on the chemical tendering of silk which led to the salvaging of hundreds of thousands of yards of rejected fabric for use in parachutes. Another area of work related to the specification of "Utility" fabrics; under War-time controls these were substantially the only apparel and domestic fabrics for which materials and production facilities were made available; the specifications were designed to give good performance with economy.

These contributions to the war effort, and others not mentioned, justified the policy of maintaining the Institute and its staff intact, but they affected only part of its work, much of which went on as if there was no war – to the frustration of some members of the staff.

Post-war reconstruction

Towards the end of the War, Sir Robert Pickard was succeeded as Director by Dr Francis Carter Toy, and he had to undertake a good deal of reconstruction both for internal and external reasons. During the War the Institute naturally lived from day to day and it now became necessary to plan for future development. The staff had also to be given sense of participation, which had been lost, if they were to make their full contribution. External to the Institute, the industry was being rehabilitated and looking to technical and managerial changes to increase productivity and improve the quality of its products. Shirley Institute was expected, and it desired, to play its full

Sir Harold Parkinson, OBE, JP, High Sheriff of Lancashire and a former Chairman of the Shirley Council, laid the foundation stone of the first post-war building, for Physics, on 14th June 1950.

The Physics and Administration Building was opened in 1953 by HRH Princess Marina, Duchess of Kent. She is seen here with Mr N.G. McCulloch, Chairman of the Shirley Council; behind are HRH Princess Alexandra of Kent and Dr F.C. Toy, Director of Research.

Dr F.C. Toy, CBE, Director of Research, 1943-55.

Dr D.W. Hill, CBE, Director of Research, 1955-69.

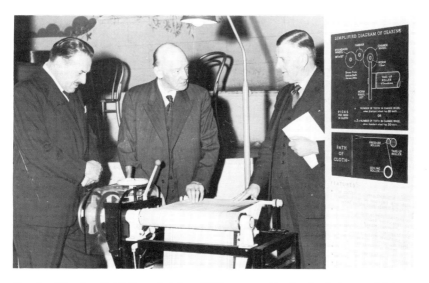

Burnley Weaving Exhibition, October 1953, arranged by the Institute to publicize its work to the industry. The photograph shows (l. to r.) Sir Harold Parkinson, Sir John Grey, and Dr F.C. Toy, Director of Research, Shirley Institute.

part in the post-war industry.

One important early step was a reorganization of the Institute's finances. Hitherto firms had paid their subscriptions voluntarily, usually through their trade associations, and although coverage was high, it was felt that some firms were benefiting indirectly from the Institute's work without having contributed to its cost. Further, higher subscription rates were seen to be necessary, and these might be expected to increase the proportion of non-payers. Consequently trade support was sought, and obtained, for a request to the Government to enact a compulsory levy on the industry. The Government through Parliament agreed, and this, through the levy collected by the Textile Council, continued to be the method by which the industry paid its contributions to the Institute's funds until 1972. At the same time the internal financial control was tightened up and a Finance Committee was established. The main instrument of control was, and is, an annual budget of projected expenditure.

A new (and in line with early post-war optimism) handsome block of buildings, put up in 1952 to house physics, testing and administration, increased the floor area by 30%.

Even in his day, when the Institute was comparatively small, Sir Robert Pickard felt the need of help in directing and administering the organization, and in 1930 Dr Toy had been appointed Deputy Director, to be joined in 1937 by Dr Douglas William Hill as an assistant. When Dr Toy became Director, Dr Hill became Deputy Director, but it was apparent that the size of the Institute and the ramifications of its activities were such that two men could not know and coordinate everything that was going on. Accordingly, in 1950 a Directorate was established consisting of the Director, Deputy Director, Secretary, and three Assistant Directors in charge respectively of research administration, the chemical departments, and mechanical and physical departments. Increasingly the Director had to attend to affairs external to the Institute, activities connected with raising funds being not the least part of these, and the new arrangement ensured that internal research work received attention from the top. The engineering services, which were becoming increasingly important and had been contained largely in the Opening and Cleaning Department, were organized in a separate department.

The Institute's involvement with the industry's reconstruction took two forms. First, the drive to make ever closer contacts with mills and works and to increase the impact of Shirley's work on their daily technical activities was intensified. Repeatedly, in the Bulletin and in speeches, mill men were exhorted to "use Shirley", and liaison officers and research staff were encouraged to give priority to dealing with Members' problems. A series of Shirley Lectures was started, surveying new developments in spinning, weaving, finishing, and in related processes. These were given in the "textile" towns. Travelling exhibitions displaying in striking ways the results of Shirley's work also visited Oldham, Burnley, Bolton, Rochdale, and Ashton-under-

Mr L.H.C. Tippett (left) received a number of awards for his work on operational research and statistics including, here, the Gilbreth Medal of the Institute of Practitioners in Work Study. Mr Tippett, a member of the Shirley staff from 1925-65, was appointed Assistant Director in charge of Mechanical Processing in 1952.

Chemistry and Finishing Building under construction, early 1960s.

HRH Princess Margaret, Countess of Snowdon, opened the Finishing Building on 21st May 1963. She is seen here with Sir Cuthbert Clegg, Chairman of Council, and (left) Dr D.W. Hill, Director of Research.

Princess Margaret's visit included a tour of other sections of the Institute, and the photograph shows Dr Kurt Greenwood explaining to her the work of the Weaving Department.

The Didsbury site prior to 1988 development, showing "The Towers" in the right foreground, and (moving clockwise) the original pre-war laboratories, the 1963 Chemistry Building, and the 1952 Physics block.

Lyne. These were attended by thousands of workpeople, foremen, managers and directors. They were very expensive, especially in the time taken by the staff in devising the exhibits and manning the shows.

Priority within the Institute was given to "special case" work and a Technical Enquiries Department was set up to deal with it. Hitherto, special case problems had been dealt with in the research departments, an arrangement that at the time had merit in familarizing research workers with the industry's problems. In time this advantage ceased to have much weight and the disadvantages of the arrangement predominated. They were that special case and other short-term work sometimes impeded the longer-term research unduly; sometimes the natural preoccupation of the research worker with his main work prevented him from dealing with a special case promptly. Often, too, a special case would require work to be done in several departments and this was administratively clumsy.

In the post-war years Lancashire looked abroad as well as at home for technical developments and the Institute had to know about these. Members of the staff made foreign visits, and this practice was developed.

Another form of involvement with the industry's reconstruction was through giving technical information to various official bodies. The Government appointed two commissions to consider systems of wage payment and work allocation to operatives in spinning and weaving, and to suggest improvements that would be fairer between operatives and would encourage efficiency and productivity. For many years the Institute had been doing surveys in mills, and the resulting store-house of information helped these commissions. As part of the campaign for improved productivity the Cotton Board (later Textile Council), among other things, arranged mill experiments to show the effects of adopting new methods of organizing the work of operatives ("redeployment" was the term used) and the Institute provided the technical assessment of the results and produced reports. Assessors were provided for committees initiated by the Factory Inspectorate on working conditions in the mills. The Institute's unrivalled knowledge of fabrics, their construction and properties, was drawn upon to assist the Cotton Board in its work of encouraging marketing. Gradually the Institute became accepted as the technical arm of the industry, to be used whenever any matter arose that had a technical content.

Behind all the activities described as belonging to the post-war period was the basic research work. This continued and extended. Many scientific and technological papers were published in learned journals. It is believed that during this period approximately one-half of the Institute's expenditure was devoted to pure and applied research, and one-half to dissemination and service work.

Dr Toy retired from the position of Director of Research in 1955 and was succeeded by Dr Hill. As Deputy Director Dr Hill had had much to do with the progress of the Institute and as Director he continued more or less along the same lines. The early years of his directorate were complicated by the negotiations that led to the amalgamation of BCIRA with BRRA.

The British Rayon Research Association

The first Director of Research was Mr John Wilson and one of his main first tasks was to build up a staff. This he had to do quickly, in the conditions of shortage of scientists that followed the War. He was able to recruit a very few experienced scientists and technologists, but the main sourse of supply was among young graduates at the universities. Consequently, there was a striking air of liveliness and enthusiasm at BRRA, and since many of the staff were unmarried and new to the district they formed a cohesive social group.

A second task was to evolve a research programme. Industrialists on research committees helped by giving advice and the Council was formally responsible, but most of the programme was due to the Director's personal inspiration and initiative, and he also participated actively in directing its conduct. The programme had a strong bias towards the fundamental and academic. One area of investigation was the structure and properties of textile

Mr John Wilson, Director of Research of the British Rayon Research Association (BRRA), 1946-58.

BRRA headquarters at Heald Green Laboratories, Wythenshawe, Manchester.

HRH Prince Philip, Duke of Edinburgh, opened the BRRA laboratories in 1955. He is seen here with the Director, Mr J. Wilson (left) and Mr Frank G. Audas.

materials, and out of this came the "infrared deuteration technique" for studying molecular order and disorder in polymers.

Considerable attention was paid to devising instruments, for use both in research and in industry, and the (then) new techniques of electronics were extensively applied. More instruments were produced than have survived in use, but one, originally devised for measuring the extent to which filament yarn is affected by protruding broken filaments, was later adapted for measuring hairiness in spun yarns of cotton as well as man-made fibre and has been of lasting practical value. It was typical of the pioneering approach of these early days that, before electronic computers became generally available, the manufacture of one was commissioned to help the research work at BRRA. It was not successful because sufficient reliability had not yet been built into computers.

Technological work was more closely directed to the industry's immediate needs, and was facilitated by extensive workrooms well-equipped with machinery for spinning, yarn preparation, weaving, finishing and (a sign of forward-looking) warp knitting. At the time the industry was installing new looms for the weaving of yarns of filament man-made fibre, and one extensive project, pursued in the workrooms at BRRA and in mills, was an assessment of the different makes of loom available. Studies of the causes of cloth defects led to a body of fundamental research work on the mechanics of cloth formation, the results of which are a part of the canon of textile literature. Much other work was done in connection with the day-to-day technical problems of Member firms.

Several exploratory attempts were made at producing new machines for use in industry, and one of these has continued to be successful. This is the application of the fluidized bed to supplying to textile materials such as yarns the heat required for some finishing processes, e.g. dyeing and heat setting.

BRRA quickly built up a range of services including a library, workshops, liaison staff, and a system of publications.

During the first decade the emphasis had been on building up BRRA – its staff, buildings, machinery and programme. Budgetary control had been introduced but more projects of research had been started than could be sustained in the long run, and by the end of the decade it was time to consider an overhaul of the administration and give the programme of work more immediacy. On 1st January 1958, Mr Leonard Albert Wiseman was appointed to succeed Mr Wilson as Director of Research to undertake these tasks. Soon, however, he became involved in the negotiations that led to the amalgamation with Shirley Institute.

The Cotton Silk and Man-made Fibres Research Association

After the amalgamation everything was looked at afresh – the name of the organization (this gave some trouble), its political structure (the composition of the Council and its committees), its finances, the staffing, the internal organization of the Institute, the research programme, and other activities. At the same time there was a strong element of continuity with BCIRA and BRRA. The people concerned and the basic needs of the industry were much the same as before, we were the constituent organizations. BCIRA had been almost twice as large as BRRA and the headquarters of the new organization at Didsbury were those of the former BCIRA; it was necessary to emphasise the fact that CSMFRA was the result of an amalgamation and not of a "take-over". Dr Hill was appointed Director of Research, and Mr Wiseman Deputy Director, and they worked to give effort to this view, and in particular to inculcate a sense of unity in the staff. Nevertheless it was in the nature of things that members of staff who came over from Heald Green should take some time to feel at home at Didsbury. Gradually the new organization became a true amalgam of the ideas and practices of both organizations.

At the start an overshadowing factor was a reduction in income. For BCIRA and BRRA together this had been about £840,000; for CSMFRA it started at about £587,000. Since salaries account for approximately 80% of the expenditure this could only be met by a reduction of staff, and by a combination of redundancy and normal wastage, the staff was reduced to 470. The redundant people were well compensated financially and many fared better in the long run but the emotional shock of being unwanted could not be cured by money; and for a time there was a sense of insecurity among those who remained. The shock was great because nothing of the sort had ever happened at Shirley before, not even during the depressing inter-war years, and the staff looked upon their jobs as being safe if not highly remunerative. Within a few months, however, the wound was cleaned up and the healing processes began, so that within two years staff morale was normally healthy.

The reduction in income and staff reduced the amount of work that could be done but there was no reduction in pressure from the industry for work. The research programme and other activities such as liaison work had to be pruned in such a way as to meet the industry's needs as fully as possible. Most of the programme was divided into discrete projects; objectives were defined as closely as possible; attempts were made to quantify the importance of each project by estimating the potential gain to the industry if it was successful or, failing that, the financial importance of the subject to the industry; and in the light of such information priorities were allocated by committees from the industry. The final programme was approved by Council. In citations accompanying the programme general objectives are stated as being to help the industry to improve productivity and quality, but these are too general to give guidance and the statement merely shows that the writers had read current industrial publicity. More influential was a subsidiary objective to give emphasis to work that would help to make Lancashire's products more saleable, and in particular to work on fabric finishing at the expense, if need be, of work on processing efficiency.

Like most similar organizations, Shirley Institute from the beginning held "open days" when people from the industry could come and see the departments and work, and talk with the staff. During the first years of CSMFRA these were held at the time of the Annual General Meeting and the attendance would be about 1,200 people of all grades from operatives to chairmen of companies. Contact between the Institute and the industry developed first and most strongly through technical managers and technologists, and with few exceptions directors, especially those on the accountancy and sales sides, had little to do with the Institute except to sign cheques for the subscriptions.

Although amalgamation resulted in a diminution in income, combination of the financial reserves of BCIRA and BRRA and the proceeds of the sale of the premises at Heald Green made large capital sums available. At that time the Institute at Didsbury was very poorly equipped with finishing machinery, so in 1963 extensive workrooms and chemical laboratories were built and equipped so as to give effect to Council's directive that more emphasis should be placed on finishing work.

This used only some of the reserves, and the DSIR (later Ministry of Technology) made it a condition of a continuation of the Government grant that the reserves should be run down further by spending the money in promoting the objects of the Association. Accordingly the programme of work was expanded and the staff increased until at one time it reached 499, and as a consequence expenditure exceeded income for some years. This could not continue for long and by 1966 new financial arrangements became necessary. It became clear that the industry, which was all the time declining in size, felt unable to increase its contributions and that from the Government correspondingly would not increase. A working party of industrialists was set up to advise on ways in which the research and services could be

Visit to Shirley Institute of staff and students from the Chemistry Department of the University of Salford in the late 1960s. Seen here (front row, l. to r.) are Dr Roy Jeffries (Shirley), Dr David M. Jones (Shirley), Professor Glyn Phillips (Salford), Dr D.W. Hill, Director of Shirley Institute and first Pro-Chancellor of the University, Professor Orville-Thomas (Salford), Dr Peter Baugh (Salford), and Dr John Honeyman, Assistant Director, Science and Technology, Shirley Institute.

The Institute's Directorate in the early 1960s. (l. to r.) Mr K.E. Lewis (Assistant Director, Finance); Dr J. Honeyman (Assistant Director, Chemistry and Chemical Processing); Mr L.A. Wiseman (Deputy Director); Dr D.W. Hill (Director of Research); Mr L.H.C. Tippett (Assistant Director, Physics and Mechanical Processing); Mr G.W. Lobb (Assistant Director, Research Administration).

reduced and economies be made so that income and expenditure would balance without any increase in compulsory contributions from the industry, but with a minimum of detriment to the industry. Its recommendations were broadly accepted and as a result the following steps were taken. The staff establishment was reduced from 475, where it stood at the time, to 390, thus subjecting the staff to a second traumatic experience of redundancies. All services to Member firms were made the subject of a charge, and the Liaison Department was disbanded, some former liaison officers being absorbed into other departments. The research programme was drastically pruned.

The change to a commercial approach to the provision of services was a great break with tradition which some members of the staff and mill managers found it hard to accept. Under the previous system a spinning manager once rang the Institute asking for a liaison officer to call and help him with a technical difficulty, and was astonished to see the liaison officer walk into the office as he was putting the 'phone down. That coincidence expresses in an extreme form the zeal with which services were provided.

The reduction in staff and research work was less than it might have been because of a growing tendency to engage in particular projects for which specific funds were contributed by outside bodies such as the United States Department of Agriculture, the National Cotton Council of America, and the International Institute for Cotton. This work was of interest to the industry served by the Institute as well as to the contributing bodies, and the results were usually published openly. In addition, sponsored work for individual companies began to be undertaken – an early example being work for Rolls Royce on textile aspects of the use of carbon fibres in aero engines. Increasingly the Institute began to earn its living from such activities.

Conclusion

Looking back over the first fifty years of the existence of Shirley Institute, with all the stresses produced by its being attached to an industry that was declining in size as well as changing in character, one is struck to see how little change there has been in the style of work done. There have been considerable changes in detail and in emphasis on different aspects, but the research was always given a good fundamental basis so that the results, however immediate in their practical application, came from a sound body of knowledge painstakingly built up. The big change has been in attitude, from regarding industrial research as a "good thing" and justifying it by faith, to regarding it as a commercail operation like any other in industry, to be justified by its works and their financial outcome, and to be administered by adaptations of the various controls and techniques that are used in other areas of management. This change has been going on in the world of applied science at large, and will doubtless continue with increasing force and effectiveness. That there are difficulties in making some of the financial assessments and in administering research, which is essentially a creative activity, does not alter the attitude.

Dr Hill retired from the position of Director of Research in March 1969 and the Institute entered its second half-century under the direction of Mr Wiseman. Its financial history has been chequered, but the present commercial approach is in accord with the spirit of the times and the future can be faced with confidence. When the Shirley Institute was formed it was one of very few textile research organizations in the world, and it built up an outstanding position. It continues to hold a position of high respect in the textile and scientific worlds.

L.H.C. Tippett

Editor's Note

The above chapter was written in 1969 for the Institute's Golden Jubilee brochure. It has been slightly modified for the present book.

Chapter II
The 1970s

The preceding account of the first fifty years of Shirley Institute concluded with the development of a more commercial attitude to the services the Institute rendered to its Members, so that such services would in future be charged for, instead of being covered by the membership fee. Writing in 1969, Mr Tippett foresaw that this trend would continue with increasing force and effectiveness and the following pages will be seen as complete endorsement of his view. The last twenty years have seen a revolution in the kind of work Shirley is undertaking, in the scientific methods it uses, its organization, and its relations with the textile industry and other clients, for its clients are no longer almost exclusively from the textile industry, and are sought and found worldwide.

In continuing the story of Shirley into the 1970s it is appropriate to consider the contents of the General Report presented by Council to the Members at the AGM in 1970. The staff at that time numbered 403. After the merger with the British Rayon Research Association on 1st April 1961 the staff numbered 499 and the loss of nearly 100 was mainly by redundancy, when it was realised that the income of the organization would not be able to support the staff it had. The total income from all sources was £800,100 of which membership subscriptions and contributions amounted to £334,000 and Ministry of Technology grants to £108,500, contracts for specific research £154,200, technical services £100,500. Total expenditure was £745,600, of which £558,000 went on research, £99,000 on accommodation and services, £59,600 on administration, plant and equipment £22,400. The history of Shirley over the next 20 years is largely the story of its struggle to maintain this small balance of income over expenditure in spite of the loss of the statutory levy, a serious depression in industry generally, combined with a decline in the Lancashire textile industry, changes in Government policy in respect of the industrial research associations, continuing and sometimes very rapid inflation, and eventually competition from other research and testing laboratories offering similar services.

In these two decades the staff has fallen to just under 200, in most years a small profit or small loss has been made and the Institute's activities have evolved and changed to meet the varying political and industrial climate.

Mr L.A. Wiseman,
Director of Research, 1969-80.

Shirley instruments on show at ITMA 71, with Mr W.T.Cowhig (centre), head of
Member Service, describing the operation of the "Shirley" Fluffing Tester.

In 1966, because of the inability of the Lancashire textile industry to maintain its contribution to central research, even sufficiently to offset inflation, it had become necessary for Shirley to review its research and financial policies. It was decided to reduce the number of central research projects, and to raise new income mainly by sponsored research and a wide range of repayment services. It was also proposed to enhance the organization's usefulness to industry by encouraging the wider use of the Institute's unique accumulation of textile knowledge and its special skills and expertise. It was further determined to strive to retain the existing staff, whose specialized knowlege and skills would otherwise be lost to industry.

To illustrate the manner in which the income of the Institute could be varied, beyond its own control, the following data are of interest. The Textile Council (which organized the statutory levy) decided to reduce its contribution for the year commencing 1969 from £295,000 to £270,000. The Ministry of Technology grant thereon was also independently reduced from $33\frac{1}{3}\%$ to 30%, that is on the reduced sum. Furthermore, as a result of a change in Ministry policy special incentive grants for selected projects would be discontinued. On the plus side, the Ministry would make a 100% grant up to a maximum of £25,000 on clothing research. This special grant was subject to the condition that it would be centrally controlled by a body representative of Shirley Institute, the Wool Industries Research Association (Wira), and the Hosiery and Allied Trades Research Association (Hatra). The Ministry would nominate to this body a number of persons representative of the clothing industry. Obviously the provision of this grant was very welcome to Shirley which had previously not been very successful in interesting the clothing industry in the services it could provide, although it would be shared with the other two RAs and the Institute would receive far less than the loss it had suffered by the reduction of the grants from the Textile Council and the Ministry.

The requirement that the three associations should cooperate to receive the clothing grant was consistent with the Ministry's general attitude. This was shown by its decision that after 1st October 1974 any grant from the Ministry of Technology made on behalf of the three industries served by the RAs would be made to a body representative of the three RAs and the Ministry would need to be satisfied that the grant would be used to support a centrally controlled programme directed to the needs of all three industries and their consumers. The Ministry had a firm commitment to a multi-fibre industry, and expected the RAs to work together in harmony with the objective.

This policy of the Ministry was quite consonant with the direction in which the three RAs were moving. These bodies had for some years taken steps, by setting up suitable committees, to avoid overlapping research programmes. In 1967 a committee (the Nottingham Committee) had been formed to promote still closer cooperation and to negotiate annual Ministry grants in support of a coordinated research programme. In due course these steps led to the setting-up of the Textile Research Council (TRC) with Mr David

Early discussion on the computerization of "World Textile Abstracts", 1969, between (l. to r.) Mr J.H. Black (editor), Mr R.J.E. Cumberbirch, Head of the Library and Information Department, and Dr K.C. Ellis, in charge of computer programming.

A view of the Finishing Workroom.

I. Griggs, Director of the Lace Research Association, as its Secretary. There had, in fact, already been a number of joint projects, on, for example, flammability of textiles, effluent treatment and water conservation, colour measurement and shade control, nonwoven fabrics, and in the preparation of World Textile Abstracts. The RAs also had representatives on each other's technical and scientific committees.

Shirley Institute policy for the 1970s was formulated in the corporate plan approved by Council in 1970. As in 1966, the importance of retaining the specialist staff was emphasised; Council expressed the intention to maintain the existing staff level, and to improve the salary structure "in order to retain and recruit research staff of a high calibre"; to orient central research towards forward-looking research on textiles more than to refinements in traditional processing; to build up research effort for the clothing industry; to achieve greater efficiency in certain aspects of administration; to improve contacts with Members and assist them in product development; to collaborate with Wira and Hatra in agreed programmes of research; to improve, if possible, conference and library capacities.

The loss of the statutory levy

In the spring of 1971 the Institute learned that its Members had decided against the continuation of the statutory levy, the product of which was being applied to central research. From 1st April 1972 central research would be supported by voluntary contributions from individual firms. This was a considerable blow to the Institute's finances and obliged it to reconsider its corporate plan. The principal effects of the loss of this source of income were on relations with Members, content of research programmes and relations with other RAs. The challenge presented by the new situation may well have had, in the long run, favourable repercussions on the course of Shirley's development but its effects were immediate and continued to be severe.

Position of Chairman

Dr Philip W. Smith was appointed as the Chairman of the Cotton Silk and Man-made Fibres Research Association and of Council at the AGM, 1971. The nature of his appointment was innovatory since, unlike previous appointments, he was given full executive powers comparable with those of a chairman in a commercial or public company. The established practice in Research Associations was to have an honorary chairman and Dr Smith's appointment was one of the steps Council was taking to cope with the new circumstances consequent on the decision of industry to change the method and level of financing Shirley Institute. Dr Smith was to continue in this position until 1988, and thus has the distinction of being the longest-serving Chairman in the Institute's history.

Institute senior executives in the 1970s: (l. to r.) Dr J. Honeyman (Assistant Director, Science and Technology); Mr L.A. Wiseman (Director of Research); Dr P.W. Smith (Chairman of Council); and Mr K.E. Lewis (Assistant Director, Finance, and Company Secretary).

Relationship with Members

The Institute was now obliged to consider what it could offer to maintain its now entirely voluntary membership at as large a level as possible. Five years earlier, in 1966, Council had decided that the product of the levy should be spent on research and not on technical services to members, since with a membership of about 1,000 the expense of a truly equitable service would be prohibitive. One cost-cutting measure was the disbandment of the annual Open Days for Member firms. These had been held for many years; in 1971 three days, 28th-30th April, were set aside for this event, and a total of 68 exhibits were arranged, virtually every laboratory being involved. However, it was to be the last such event as the staff time involved in both preparation and participation was considerable and it was realised that the cost of this was unduly high in view of reduced membership income. About this time, to replace the Liaison Department a new technical liaison service was set up, in which Members would receive, for a basic minimum subscription, the following services: (a) access to the Institute's confidential research programme, including receipt of confidential publications: (b) consultations, free or at preferential rates, according to the circumstances; (c) technical investigations, sponsored research projects and development work at preferential rates; (d) preferential rates for a wide range of quality control and testing services; (e) access to a very full information service; (f) preferential rates for most Shirley publications; (g) attendance at Shirley seminars and conferences; (h) opportunities to send staff on training courses; (i) twice-yearly technical liaison visits by senior members of staff. The early response to these new membership arrangements was that 4 out of the 5 large textile groups, and about 120 of the medium and small firms, continued in membership (this rose eventually to about 170, augmented by firms from Europe and USA).

Future research programme

It was decided that in the new circumstances central research would be in four areas:

(1) Information services for all sectors of industry. These would be based on World Textile Abstracts (WTA), a twice-monthly periodical which summarizes all world literature. Before 1974, it was decided, WTA databases would be made compatible with the computer information services of the large firms and central organizations, and an information retrieval system would be made available to all firms. Members would also have access to internally generated but unpublished information including a large quantity of marketing and economic information.

(2) Performance design of textile products for all sections of the industry. This was already a growing field at the Institute.

(3) Research on technical aspects of garment manufacture, in collaboration with Hatra and Wira, with Government support as described earlier.

(4) Selected areas of dyeing and finishing. It was expected that these would include colour measurement of dyed yarns and fabrics, reduction of shade variations, treatment of effluent, and improved utilization of water.

Financial policy at this period had been influenced by three factors – the decision of the Textile Council to reduce its contributions to the Institute from £295, 000 to £270, 000 and the consequential reduction in the grant from the Department of Trade and Industry (DTI); the uncertainty of the level of support to be expected from industry; and the effects of rapid inflation. To meet these circumstances policy was based on the following decisions:

(1) For the time being the scale of the Institute's central research and services to industry would remain at the reduced level already reached.

(2) The loss of income and the effects of inflation should be met as far as possible by an extension of repayment work, the development of the site at Didsbury, and the acceptance into membership of firms in Western Europe and N. America.

(3) Such further economies were to be made as was possible without reducing the Institute's earning capacity.

(4) Any shortfall was to be met from reserves.

In fact, because of changes in circumstances it proved impossible to adhere to this policy for very long. It became clear that contributions from the Textile Council would be reduced. Furthermore, the growth in the income from contracts for specific research and investigations ceased and then reversed. This was considered to be due entirely to the ecomomic climate, and indeed it proved to be temporary, but it reinforced the view that further economies should be made. The most important saving was to be selective non-replacement of staff, that is, the losses of staff that normally occur due to leaving or retirement were not to be made good except for key vacancies. This brought about a reduction of staff from 371 to 325.

The financial outlook for the Institute was so bleak that the British Textile Employers' Association, together with other Trade Assocations and Trade Unions, set up an Ad hoc Committee "to ascertain the circumstances under which the Shirley Institute might carry on its work after 31st March 1972" (i.e. when the levy would cease). It was concluded that "from 1973 onwards the Institute should be entirely dependent upon voluntary contributions from the widest area together with income derived from sponsored research and its earning power in other fields". It was decided that from 1st April 1972 central research and associated services would be funded by the individual contributions of those firms which decided to continue their membership.

An unavoidable consequence of the financial stringency was that more than 20% of the staff had to be declared redundant on 31st March 1972. Part of the Institute's reserves were used to provide compensation for redundant staff. Those remaining numbered 250.

Council decided that its future policy would be based on the following objectives:

(1) to establish the Institute as a world centre of excellence in selected fields, offering the highest level of development and technological services, arising from its prime research attributes.

(2) the continuance and expansion of the special relationship already existing between the "Lancashire" textile industry and its associated industries, towards which the central research, development, and technological activities would continue to be directed.

(3) the expansion of Shirley research, development and technological activities in any other industries, both within and outside the UK, where the accumulated knowledge and expertise could be usefully applied.

In the year during which the statutory levy ceased, the Institute did in fact receive the levy for 6 months, and the Textile Council made a special contribution of £50,000 which became available on the dissolution of that body. In addition the voluntary membership scheme brought in an income of £127,000, the number of medium and smaller firms entering into membership having risen to 170. There was also a welcome increase in repayment income over the previous year (which had been a disappointing year) resulting from a rise in the level of confidential sponsored research projects and advisory services. The financial position of the Institute was, on the whole, better than had been expected, and the deficit was only £8,520.

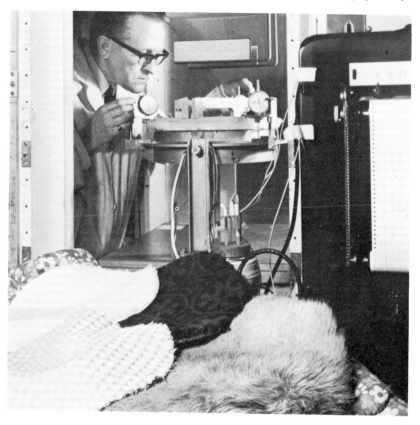

Mr Howard Rees, pictured c. 1970 with the "Shirley Togmeter which he devised for measurement of the thermal insulation of textiles.

The results of efforts to bring into membership firms in Europe and N. America were encouraging, firms in Denmark, Finland, Germany, Holland and Switzerland having already joined. The income from this source was as yet small, but was an indication of the international recognition of the standing of the Institute, and therefore a legitimate cause for optimism. A marketing investigation to identify openings for Shirley's services, particularly contract work and advisory and consultative services, was encouraging and indicated that there would be a continuing demand for this work. On the other hand, the market in the UK for these services outside the textile machinery industries was unlikely to be large enough, necessitating efforts to enlarge overseas membership and contracts.

After 31st March 1972

The financial year to September 1973 would be the first year completely without the levy, and expectations were therefore that a loss would be inevitable. In the event the outcome was a surplus of approximately £41,000, far better than had seemed at all possible. Three factors had contributed to this happy result. The first was the large increase in effort that had been put into marketing the skills and expertise of the staff. The second was that industrial activity during this period had improved, and that these efforts therefore fell on fertile ground. The third reason was not one to give any pleasure: as a result of a tight rein on staff costs, there was a greater number than usual of unfilled vacancies. Steps were taken to improve staff remuneration and recruitment.

The increase in the income from repayment services was the most important of these three factors. Income from contract work was £264,000, an increase of 42% on the previous year. Income for technical service work, which includes advisory and consultative services, conferences, courses and publication sales was nearly £194,000, up by 27% on the previous year.

In September 1973 the Institute's order book for contract and technical work was fuller than it ever had been and the trend was still favourable. This position owed much to the specialized knowledge accumulated during years of research. However it was recognized that during the past few years this store had not been replenished sufficiently to cope with the problems that the textile industry would face in the next decade. There was a pressing need, therefore, for an increase in research effort, both to obtain new information and for the staff to become involved in the demands of the future.

The following year saw events unfolding rather better than expected. A surplus of £25,000 was recorded, largely attributable to a 53% increase in the return from sponsored research. Income from technical and advisory services was up 20% on the previous year. Salaries and wages were increased to a more appropriate level, which had not been possible in earlier years because of legislative restraints.

Serious thought was now being given to extension of the Institute's activities to the developing countries. For many years, of course, the membership would not have allowed this, on the grounds that it would be giving assistance to the UK textile industry's competitors (an objection that also was applied to working for European and American firms). This attitude had now been modified for it was realised that, apart from humanitarian considerations, it was a benefit to all that the development of the backward countries should be hastened. It could also be justified as making a small contribution to the UK balance of "invisible" trade. Shirley began to pursue these possibilities with the proviso that it would not act in such a way as to cause material damage to the UK industry.

The Institute's longest-running training course, on card grinding, has been held several times per year since the early 1970s, under the direction of Mr K.L. Floyd.

Group of long-serving Engineering Department staff, January 1976, Front row, seated, l. to r., Mr R.I. Davis, Mrs J. Robins, Mr H. Taylor, Mr A. Linnert. Standing, l. to r., Mr F. Oliver, Mr J. Page, Mr F.A. Thompson, Mr F. Tippman, Mr J. Maguire, Mr C. Yeoward, Mr K. Richardson, Mr F. Jackson, Mr F. Hackland.

The Rothschild Principle

In 1975 there was a major change in the principles controlling the funding, by Government Departments, of the Research Associations. Previously, a Government Department would make grants that were not specific to particular research, but were related to the size of the industrial contribution to the RA's cooperative research activities. The new principle, referred to as the Rothschild Principle since it was enumerated in the Rothschild Report "A Framework for Government Research & Development", November 1971, as accepted by the Government was that Government grants for research should be allocated to specific research projects, that is, there should be a customer-contractor relationship between the Department and its own research establishments. Although this report applied specifically to Government research establishments, it was extended to the Research Associations which received support from the Department of Industry. This apparently reasonable provision was eventually to have unfortunate consequences. To implement the Rothschild Principle, the Department of Industry, which was responsible for the provision of funds to the textile industry Research Associations, set up a number of Requirements Boards, which were, in effect, to act as the customer. The Textile Research Council put forward the view that the textile industry, together with related industries producing clothing, footwear and leather, and the industries supplying production machinery for these industries, formed a group large enough to have its own Requirements Board, a view accepted by the DoI which responded by setting up the Garment and Allied Industries Requirements Board (GARB).

1975-1980

In 1975, instead of a small surplus, as in the two previous years, the Institute ended the financial year with a deficit of over £3,000. The principal contributing factor to this was the lower-than-expected income from sponsored research, most probably attributable to the worldwide economic recession that developed during the course of the year. The accompanying textile depression was particularly severe and impinged on the Institute's progress both at home and overseas. This led to changes in the emphasis of the Institute's overall policy, as established on the loss of the statutory levy. These included measures to bring about worldwide increase in the utilization of the Institute's research and development potential; extension of overseas membership beyond Western Europe and America (bringing the Institute in line with others RAs); and most regrettably again, the selective non-replacement of staff.

For the next year it was possible to report a surplus of £34,000, arising largely from an increase of £9,800 in repayment work; under this heading there had been a continually increasing return for 6 years. It was believed, however, that escalating overheads based on continuing inflation would eventually outstrip all possible increases in repayment work, in the conditions under which the Institute was working, at home and abroad. It was vital to find a remedy for this situation. As usual at times of crisis the possibilities of easing the situation by capitalizing on the Didsbury site were considered, including the options of abandoning it entirely, or sharing it more effectively. No acceptable solution based on such means was found. An alternative would be to expand the Institute's operations to a new level, by increasing the staff to 300, and developing the Institute into an international research organization. Further cooperative work with other RAs was also possible, for example, on water usage, effluent control and energy economy. Although the Institute was not in immediate financial trouble it was essential to give very serious consideration to the future.

A profit of £74,000 was made in 1976-77, attributable again to increases in repayment work, but this profit was largely offset by inflation. Salaries had for some time not been competitive with those paid by comparable employers, so in order to make increases, permission was obtained from the Central Arbitration Committee, to exceed the statutory maximum then in force.

In June 1977 delegates from Wira and Shirley Institute met to determine whether the two RAs could be brought together in one organization, but in February 1978 discussions were discontinued at the request of the Shirley Council. Their view was that if a research operation for the whole of the textile industries was to be established at that time, it would certainly not be logical to set up separate centres. Starting, however, from the position of 1978 the main difficulty arose from the fact that Shirley had been operating under different financial constraints from the other textile RAs, subsequent to the aboliton of the levy. Shirley Institute did not rely now on direct industrial support for its central research; such support represented only 8% of its total income, and this fraction was being reduced year by year. The relationship that Shirley had with industry was not comparable with that which Wira had with the Yorkshire industry, since Wira's membership comprised a much larger number of smaller companies. Council's eventual view was that the existing arrangements for cooperation in textile research were to be preferred to the many difficulties that a merger could produce.

Retirement of Mr Wiseman

Mr L.A. Wiseman, who had been Director since April 1969, was to retire in 1980. In seeking a successor the Institute took the view that although it was well staffed with scientists and technologists there was a clear shortage of marketing experience. Mr Kenneth A. Mitchell, who was selected for this position, had training and experience in the marketing field. He assumed the position of Managing Director on 1st April 1980, with Dr John Honeyman, who had been at Shirley since 1956, being appointed Director of Research. At this time an Executive Board was established in order to make executive decisions – a function that previously had been partially filled by delegated members of Council; Council would continue to hold responsibility for final decisions on major policy concerns. The new arrangements required a change in the Articles of Association and were marked also by a change of name, Henceforth "Shirley Institute" would be the new official name, just as it had for long been the only name by which the organization had been known to many. The title of "The Cotton Silk and Man-made Fibres Research Association" was dropped completely.

It had become evident, from the way in which membership contributions had failed to keep pace with inflation whereas payment for contract research was increasing, that firms preferred to pay for work specific to their requirements. There were some problems that were of interest to a few, or several, firms, but not to the majority of Members. For some time the Institute had run market survey projects, to which a number of firms had contributed funds. This multi-sponsor approach was now to be extended to research projects. The Requirements Board, GARB, referred to earlier, was willing to support projects of this type.

In the first year following these changes (1980-1), an exceptionally large loss of £158,324 was returned, quite out of line with the modest gains or losses of previous years. This loss was associated with a shortfall in receipts for sponsored research, the sums received being £920,000 whereas £1.1 million had been budgeted for. Practically all other items accorded with the budget. The disappointing return from sponsored research was a reflection of the difficult time that industry was experiencing. It was also ascribable to the operation of the Rothschild Principle, whereby Government grants were to be made for specific projects only. In periods of recession, when sponsors were liable to economize on research projects, assistance from Government Departments also was reduced, at a time when it was most needed.

H.M. Taylor

Chapter III
The 1980s

During 1981-82 it became increasingly obvious that conventional marketing wisdom, though effective for tangible consumer products, was not suited to the marketing of scientific research, and that the 1980 appointment of a Managing Director with marketing skills but without in-depth knowledge of industrially oriented research was unlikely to provide the answer to Shirley's problems. The change in attitude, forced on the Institute after the cessation of the levy, had been dramatic and very fundamental; the speed with the Council and staff strove to come to terms with this change underlines the difficulties inherent in adjusting to the additional imposition of a totally new marketing approach, to which technical staff were intrinsically antipathetic.

In April 1982 a new Managing Director, Alasdair Maclean, who had held a senior position in industrial research and development, was appointed in place of Kenneth Mitchell who had left the Institute in December 1981. Mr L.A. Wiseman, the previous Director of Research, and Dr John Honeyman, Asssistant Director, who had both given many years of service to the Institute, had retired. During that year as a result of the stringent control of costs, rather than the generation of a substantial increase in income, the loss of the previous year was converted into a small profit. There was a 30% increase in Technical Service work, which included advisory and consultative services, conferences and courses, and the sale of publications. Another welcome growth area was the use of Institute staff as consultants in connection with a range of Government schemes, for example, the Manufacturing Advisory Scheme operated though the Production Engineering Research Association and Salford University Industrial Centre, the Small Firms Technical Enquiry Service, the Quality Assurance Advisory Service and the Microprocessor Awareness Scheme. But contracts for sponsored research in fact fell to £860,000. The work sponsored by individual firms was described as "alarmingly small and falling".

The new Managing Director had to deal with a position where it was clear that a way had not yet been found of ensuring the long-term prosperity of the Institute. Investment income had all but disappeared. No acceptable way of realising the capital value of the site had so far been found – being part of a Conservation Area, its use was subject to restrictions. The management structure derived largely from what was appropriate in the early days of the Institute; the established Divisions and Departments no longer corresponded closely enough to the pattern of the work. A completely new arrangement

Executive Board of Shirley Institute, July 1980: (l. to r.) Mr A.N. Benson (Woodhey Dyeing Co. Ltd); Dr J. Honeyman (Director of Research, Shirley Institute); Mr K. A. Mitchell (Managing Director, Shirley Institute); Mr W. Barnes (formerly of Carrington Viyella Ltd); Mr L.A. Wiseman (Shirley Institute). (Mr Benson and Mr Barnes continued to serve as non-executive Directors of Shirley Institute until 1988.)

was now adopted, whereby the staff was organized into 6 Technical Groups, comprising 17 Business Centres, each with its own budget. To increase staff participation in the running of the Institute, two members of the staff, one to represent management (Dr Brian F. Sagar), and one to act as staff observer (Mr K. L. Floyd), were nominated to Council.

In a policy document of October 1982 the new Managing Director proposed that in the next 2-3 years the Institute's aim should be tactical survival to allow breathing space for establishment of an exploitation strategy for the Institute's existing resources – people, equipment, property, as well as specialist knowledge, business goodwill, reputation. Survival thus far had been achieved at very considerable cost, by non-investment in replacement resource. There had been strict control of discretionary costs and avoidance of activities which did not directly generate income. Progress was further hindered by external economic conditions as well as by the Institute's low income, high overheads (especially the site), and the effects of the lack of capital expenditure over the past ten years.

The long-term mission of the Institute was declared as follows: "To be a profitable provider of high-quality contract services appropriate to the needs initially of the textile industry on a worldwide base, and expanding as sensible opportunities are identified in other areas".

In addition to exploiting the capital assets of the Institute more determined efforts were made, with some success, to exploit its intellectual property, by arranging licences with external companies and organizations on the basis of past patents and completed project work.

The financial year 1983/4 brought what was described as the " first authentic profit the Institute has made in the past four years". £5,808 on a turnover of £2.86 million, as compared with a loss in the preceding year of

Dr Alasdair Maclean,
Managing Director, Shirley Institute
(1982-88)

£43,372 on a turnover of £2.43 million.

An important feature of Shirley's current activities, multi-client sponsored research projects, began to become the norm for the central research programme. The idea that for a modest initial outlay sponsoring firms could obtain the results of work costing up to 40 times that figure to execute, proved attractive to a wide range of clients, though the larger firms predominated. Many of them see these joint projects as an adjunct to their own in-house research, especially in the more innovative areas of work; the smaller and medium-sized companies are less inclined to commit a proportion of their limited funds to such projects which necessarily carry no guarantee of short-term profits.

Income from multi-sponsor projects was £200,000 in 1983/4 but fell disappointingly to £141,000 in the following year. No major factor was responsible but management saw the downturn as due in part to the ever-increasing competition from other providers of contract services.

From 1983 onwards, the Institute began to adopt a more vigorous and outgoing approach to marketing its services, trying new publicity techniques such as a lightweight tabloid newspaper "Insight", more advertizing and editorial coverage in the trade and general press, more frequent participation in technical conferences and exhibitions, and direct mailing of the list of current and planned projects to potential clients in several countries. These concerted efforts began to pay off, as evidenced by the 250% increase in contributions from UK industrial clients in 1985, by comparison with two years previously.

The years 1984/5/6 all proved difficult, largely because of the shortage of funded project work. However technical services work has continued to grow; in 1985/6 income under the general heading exceeded £1 million for the first time, having more than doubled over the previous five years. A major boost to the testing facilities was the NATLAS accreditation gained in 1985/6 (discussed later under "Testing Services").

But still the problem of having a too large, too expensive-to-maintain site remained, and increasingly this excessive overhead was seen as the main obstacle to the establishment of a viable cost base for the Institute.

Shirley Developments Ltd

During 1986 the ownership of Shirley Developments Ltd was transferred to its Executive Directors, and at the same time a revised trade-mark and royalty agreement was concluded with Shirley Institute, under which the latter would benefit from the continuing growth of SDL. Mention has been made elsewhere in this book of the active collaboration between SDL and the Institute, and an increasing number and range of instruments is being made in the Institute's Instrumentation, Microelectronics, and Engineering workrooms.

The establishment of Shirley Developments Ltd (SDL) in 1951 was an event of more than local interest since it represented a pioneering approach to the application of research results in industry. The company is well known as a supplier of textile testing equipment, and now markets the instrument ranges of several manufacturers as well as those emanating from Shirley.

Dr B.F. Sagar, representative of Institute Management on Shirley Council, 1982-88.

Mr K.L. Floyd, staff observer on Shirley Council, 1982-88.

AGM of Shirley Developments Ltd, 1968, showing (l. to r.) Dr D.W. Hill, Director of Research, Shirley Institute; Sir Raymond Streat, Chairman of SDL; and Mr Hugh Wyn Griffith, General Manager of SDL.

Physics and Administration Building (1952), later re-named "Scotscroft".

Although SDL was set up by Shirley Institute, and was formally linked for many years, it is now a fully independent company.

Over the years, many new instruments have been developed at Shirley, some with fairly narrow application for a specific job, others with much wider potential. By the 1950s a considerable demand had grown up from industry, and the manufacture, patenting, and supply of these instruments were all proving burdensome to the staff whose main duties and expertise lay in research. An additional factor was that Government regulations did not permit Research Associations to exploit their work for profit. It was felt during this post-war reconstruction period that a more commercial approach should be adopted, both for the industry's benefit and for the income that would accrue to the Institute.

The idea for a separate commercial company to develop, make, and sell Shirley instruments was put forward by the late Sir Raymond Streat KBE and fellow members of an Exploitation Committee, which had been set up by the Shirley Institute Council in 1949.

The proposal was regarded at the time as a most unusual, even daring experiment in the technique of bringing innovations into industry. However, subsequent events have proved the concept was a good one and, with its growing expertise in this specialist activity, SDL went on to take over the marketing of instruments for other research associations and companies. Sir Raymond Streat became SDL's first Chairman, a post he held for 20 years, and Mr K.E. Lewis, Shirley Institute's Company Secretary, acted in the same capacity for SDL. The first General Manager was Mr John Oram, followed in the mid-1950s by Mr Hugh Wyn Griffith, and he was succeeded by Mr Russell Crompton in 1984.

In recent years SDL has expanded considerably, and has achieved a high public profile through advertising and participation in exhibitions. It is now one of the world's largest suppliers of textile testing equipment, with the ability to fulfil orders from a single instrument to a complete testing laboratory.

Utilization of the site

Since about the mid-1960s part of the Shirley buildings surplus to current needs were let off as office and storeroom accommodation to selected tenants, mostly small companies engaged in professional, scientific, or technical work. This yielded valuable income from the conveniently located, attractive site and indeed by 1981/2 Shirley's income from such lettings exceeded that from industrial membership subscriptions.

A major step forward in this process was taken during 1981-3 when Shirley vacated the Physics and Administration Building. "The Towers" (usually until this time referred to by staff as "the House", and occupied solely by the Library and Information Department) was extensively refurbished, the attic floors were reclaimed from the spiders and pigeons, and new paint was much in evidence throughout. The Reception Desk and main administrative offices,

Shirley staff, November 1987.

together with additional technical staff, moved into The Towers. The 1952 Physics Building, soon re-named Scotscroft after a house previously on the same site, took in still more tenants.

After several years of discussions and negotiations with the local authorities, property and development experts, and other interested parties including local amenity, civic and residents' representatives, 1988 saw the culmination of this long-drawn-out process.

In April 1988 Shirley announced the sale of the entire site to Intercity Property Group, for development as a high-technology business park, under the title "Towers 2000".

Thus the house, in which Shirley started in 1919, provides the focal point for wider industrial development, whilst it remains the administrative centre for textile research.

Shirley remains on the site as a long-term leaseholder of part of the grounds and a new laboratory block to be built adjacent to its headquarters, "The Towers". There are plans to move some of the heavier industrial activities to another location in Greater Manchester.

The merger with Wira

In the mid-1980s the ongoing deliberations on how to ensure the Institute's future profitability had led again to the idea of a merger with Wira Technology Group (formally the Wool Industries Research Association), which had been established in Leeds since 1918.

Now that the sharp fibre-use divisions in the textile industry were becoming more blurred, and with the overall decrease in the industry's size and the likely reduction in the level of future Government financial support, there was a danger that the two very similar bodies would be competing, disadvantageously to both, for the same funding and clients.

An external organization was retained, with sponsorship from the Department of Trade and Industry, to investigate the practicalities of a merger between the two bodies. Guided by Profile Consultancy's positive report, the Council of Shirley and the Board of WTG announced in June 1987 that a merger would take place subject to satisfactory detailed agreement and their Members' approval. To implement their plans the two ruling bodies appointed an Executive Chairman Designate, Mr J. Harry Leach, who had just completed a two-year term as President of the British Textile Confederation. He took up his post on 1st August 1987, with the result that legal formalities to effect the merger were completed on 1st October 1988. The new organization thus formed bears the name "British Textile Technology Group".

At the AGM in July 1988, the Chairman of Shirley, Dr Philip W. Smith OBE, said: "BTTG will coordinate and build on the strengths of the two research bodies, and will be a multi-fibre, multi-process R&D group, with a worldwide client base. We look forward to the future with renewed confidence."

Maureen Sawbridge

Executive Committee of Shirley Institute, in office until the formation of BTTG, 1988. Seated, l. to r., Mr A. Lawless, Dr A. Maclean, Dr D.M. Jones; standing, l. to r., Dr B.F. Sagar, Mr R.J.E. Cumberbirch, Dr R. Jeffries. (There have also been two Non-executive Directors, Mr A.N. Benson and Mr W. Barnes.)

HRH The Princess Royal visited the Shirley stand at the 1988 "Textile and Technology" exhibition in Manchester. She is seen here with Dr A. Maclean, Managing Director, Shirley Institute.

Chapter IV
The Work of the Institute

During its almost 70 years of existence Shirley has striven to assist the textile industry. But that industry has, over the years, been subject to major changes, in the fibres it deals with, and in the processes and machinery it employs, and the Institute's close involvement in this evolution has caused it, too, to vary the emphasis of its work.

Improvements in the quality and uniformity of raw materials, coupled with the impact of advanced machinery design incorporating microelectronics technology, have made the textile industry, in common with most other modern industries, much less labour-intensive and more highly productive.

Starting in 1919 with cotton alone, then in 1936 adding silk, and later (especially after the merger with BRRA) turning its attention to viscose and the newer synthetic fibres, Shirley Institute ranks among the world's foremost textile research and development centres. Membership is open to organizations in the UK and overseas that have an interest in fibres, polymers, textiles, clothing, and related manufactures; and work is also done for non-Member firms.

An overview of Shirley Institute's work today can be gained by looking at its main activities and the pattern of their development.

Spinning, Weaving, Nonwovens

The processing of textile fibres into fabrics is an aspect of Shirley's activities that has undergone the kind of revolution that would have been virtually impossible to foresee some 20 years ago. In contrast to the scene as described by Mr Tippett in 1969, when spinning machinery was much in evidence in the workrooms, the emphasis has changed in response to the industry's needs, so that the work relevant to yarn production is now mainly confined to the assessment of natural and man-made fibres and yarns, and associated small-scale spinning trials.

Much more attention nowadays is being paid to fabric production by "nonwoven" methods, that is, directly from fibres without the need to spin yarns as an intermediate step. The Institute took an early lead and since 1971 its work on the preparation of the card web has led to major contributions to the development of nonwovens technology, especially thermal bonding. A comprehensive range of equipment is now installed in the Nonwovens workroom. The choice of equipment for thermal bonding is dictated by the

Mr J Mitchell (left) of Shirley Institute inspecting a new variety of cotton at the cotton breeding station at Wad Medani in the Sudan, 1986, as part of a consultancy project.

A Shirley training course on nonwovens production.

properties required in the end-product. Thus, calenders (heated steel rollers) are used for lightweight, compacted materials of the sort intended for disposable nappies and incontinence pads, while hot-air ovens are preferred for the low-density, non-compacted types used for thermal insulation. Ultrasonic equipment for nonwoven bonding is also available at Shirley. In the work undertaken for clients there is considerable emphasis on "engineering" of nonwovens for specific, usually high-added-value, applications for industrial and technical, rather than apparel, uses.

In recent years, the Weaving workroom has concentrated on the design of woven structures to meet clients' particular needs. As an example, a special fabric was designed as a component in a complex aircraft windshield construction, in a collaborative project with a leading safety glass manufacturer. The brief, to provide a windshield mounting that combined very high breaking strength with good flexibility, to exacting engineering standards, was successfully met by the development of a woven fabric from rubber-coated Fibreglass and stretch nylon yarns; this fabric component subsequently went into commercial use in the Boeing 747 aircraft.

Carbon, PTFE, aramids, and other difficult-to-handle fibres are commonly dealt with in the Weaving workroom, and commission weaving, especially for short-run and experimental projects, is undertaken.

Dyeing and Finishing

Work in this area consists of both R&D and commission dyeing and finishing. The R&D group offers expertise both in processing (preparation, dyeing, printing, chemical and mechanical finishing) and in the equipment used to carry out such processing. There is emphasis on innovation, evaluation and efficiency, and on the development of new technologies, including technology transfer from other disciplines.

Newer processing techniques being studied in the laboratories include low-liquor ratio dyeing, the use of foam as a transfer medium, creasing in jet dyeing, radio frequency heating for drying and dye fixation. In collaboration with the Institute's Colour Physics staff, work is in progress on all aspects of automatic colour measurement and control of coloration.

Conservation of water, chemicals, and energy are key factors in many of the dyeing and finishing projects at Shirley. One embodiment of these aims, arising from the Institute's work in collaboration with a UK textile machinery maker, is the Steam Purge System, which has proved its worth in extensive pilot-scale and industrial trials. In principle, the system involves driving the air out of a fabric and replacing it with steam; this facilitates complete wetting-out in the impregnation of textile materials. The system is now operating successfully in several countries for preparation, dyeing, and finishing of cotton and polyester/cotton fabrics. As well as saving energy, use of the steam purge system cuts down the consumption of water, dyes, and chemicals, reduces the criticality of the preparation stages, and improves the final product quality.

The Dyeing and Finishing Workroom provides for the textile industry a service it is no longer keen to provide for itself, namely, processing of short runs and difficult-to-handle fabrics, reprocessing of damaged or faulty (especially imported) goods, and the like. Turnover in the Workroom has increased dramatically over the past decade; in the last financial year turnover exceeded £400,000 for the first time and a 15% increase compared with the previous year was recorded. A very wide range of fabric types is handled, including both staple and filament wovens, knits, and nonwovens. There is currently a high level of demand for flame-retardant finishing, to meet impending UK legislative requirements.

The Workroom also handles narrow-width coating and impregnation, and a recently added facility is for adhesive lamination.

Energy

Of all stages of textile production, the finishing sector is the largest user of energy because of the frequent fabric wetting and drying involved in its processes. More than 90% of the energy used is commonly in the form of heat, and there is also a close relationship between energy and water usage. These facts have shaped the pattern of work on energy at Shirley, both as regards the research projects undertaken and the consultancy services provided to industrial firms.

Shirley was entrusted with the direction and execution of the energy thrift and audit surveys in the textile, leather, and clothing industries, initiated by the Department of Energy of the UK Government in the 1970s, largely as a response to the oil crisis.

Whilst the emphasis of the Shirley work has been on energy management in the textile finishing sector, the same principles have also been applied to synthetic fibre production and to spinning and weaving. Frequently, comparatively small modifications to existing procedures or equipment have resulted in rationalization of energy use, giving economies way beyond the cost of the changes.

The energy work has been recognized by the 1988 award of the Silver Medal of the Society of Dyers and Colourists to Dr John G. Roberts.

Textile Products

Institute work on textile products embraces apparel, domestic, and industrial textiles.

The research programme and services relate to the properties and behaviour of clothing fabrics, primarily functional garments for workwear and foul-weather protection. Very high performance is demanded nowadays for industrial workwear, in such aspects as flammability and heat protection, "static" propensity, comfort and "breathability", water repellency, and

Dr John Roberts (right) responsible for Energy work at Shirley, with Mr David Hunt, MP, Parliamentary Under-Secretary of State for Energy, on the occasion of the signing of an agreement for Shirley to introduce energy monitoring and target setting into the Finishing sector of the textile industry, 8th October 1984.

Early work on energy conservation, 1974. Dr Colin Reed checks the performance of a water/water heat exchanger at a Member firm.

Mr. W.J. Morris, inventor of the "Positorq", and assistant Mrs Joan Jackson in the Institute's yarn texturing workroom, 1976.

durability. In recent years, the functional aspects of everyday clothing, too, have grown in importance, thermal underwear and sportswear being notable examples, and this is reflected in the type of work undertaken.

Research is also done on textiles for use in the home, public buildings, hospitals, and hotels, in particular, bedding, furnishings, upholstery fabrics, and curtains.

Many of the investigations are, and have been, done for Government Departments–the Ministry of Defence, Department of Health and Social Security, for public authorities (e.g. the Fire Service), and for official bodies such as the King Edward's Hospital Fund and the Disabled Living Foundation. The expertise gained in these investigations, and often the technology or methods developed in connection with them, are, with the permission of the original sponsoring body, subsequently applied to general consumer products.

The design and development of new and improved products are a major feature of the work, as well as the evaluation and testing of existing products.

A Textile Products Division was first set up at Shirley in 1970 and the aims and objectives then laid down continue to form the basis of the work in this field. A statement to Members at the time indicated that a multi-disciplinary team would be employed on this work, and that special emphasis would be placed upon "an integrated approach which takes into account choice of fibre, method of fabrication, and conversion into end-product, regardless or whether the product involved be clothing, furnishing fabric, carpet, (or) industrial material".

A similar approach is taken to the whole range of industrial textiles – sometimes called "technical fabrics". In particular, the staff have developed expertise in fibre-reinforced composites, filtration, and yarn texturing.

One important commercial outcome of Shirley work on yarn texturing in the 70s was the Scragg "Positorq" friction twisting unit for false-twist yarn texturing. This confounded the previous general belief that friction twisting without slip was impossible, when by relatively simple but fundamental changes in the geometry of existing disc-twisting units W.J. Morris developed a new unit, the Positorq, which could operate in a no-slip mode. The industrial sponsors of the research sold large quantities of the unit and most of the false-twist texturing machines on show at the 1975 ITMA exhibition incorporated units based on the Shirley invention. W.J. Morris was subsequently honoured with an MBE and with the S.G. Smith Memorial Medal of the Textile Institute, in recognition of this work.

In the fibre-reinforced composites field, a family of machines for making composite pre-preg sheets has been developed, which enable manufacture to be speeded up by at least a factor of 5 compared with conventional techniques.

Gas and liquid filtration have been subjects for research at Shirley, with particular reference to energy economies, filtration efficiency, and improvement of filter fabrics.

Materials Science

A prime target of research in many industries in the 1980s is the development of new materials with enhanced performance characteristics. The Shirley work on materials science reflects this trend, in covering the analysis, chemical modification, and structure-reactivity relationships of natural and synthetic polymers. The work for the textile and allied industries is concerned with novel fabric coatings and finishes, flame-retardancy, and the behaviour of polymers in hostile environments.

A major success story arising from the work of Dr. J. R. Holker and Dr. G. R. Lomax is the Shirley-Baxenden "breathable" fabric, which is now being marketed worldwide for sportswear and foul-weather clothing. Originally developed in a Shirley project for the Ministry of Defence, this innovative non-microporous polyurethane coating permits the passage of evaporated sweat from the body of the wearer yet at the same time remains waterproof to rain. This is a good example of a technical advance which was first designed for military purposes but which, subsequent to release for civilian use, has been patented and licensed to a UK company for commercial exploitation.

Shirley/Baxenden breathable coated fabric in use for ski wear. The photograph shows the US National Barefoot Water Skiing Champion, 1987.

Though the research programme centres on textile applications, work on wider aspects of plastics and polymer chemistry and technology is increasing.

Biotechnology

Biodeterioration, the adverse effects of bacteria and micro-organisms, as occurs for example when mildew attacks untreated cotton tents, is a well known phenomenon. Since Shirley's early days the staff have sought ways of preventing microbial attack of this kind; one such solution was the development in the 1920s of Shirlan, an anti-mildew treatment for cotton.

The Institute provides a service for assessment of the susceptibility of materials to microbial attack and for evaluation of the efficacy of commercial biocide treatments. A considerable amount of work has been done at Shirley on polyurethanes, which were at first thought to be immune to biodegradation; the work has shown that this is not the case, and has elucidated the conditions under which they are susceptible to microbial attack.

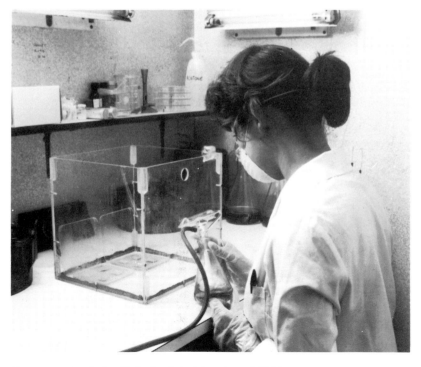

Spore spraying in the Biotechnology laboratory at Shirley.

The reverse side of the coin is the harnessing of the biosystems to yield desirable results, under the general heading of "biotechnology". Indeed, before the advent of this modern fashionable term, the textile industry had used bacteria and enzymes for many years as processing aids. A classic example is the removal of starch from loomstate cloth, which depends on the action of an enzyme that converts the insoluble starch to soluble sugar.

Shirley's Biotechnology staff have long been involved in the enzymology of cellulose and other polysaccharides, and with the development of fungal and bacterial fermentation as a means of producing specific enzymes for utilization in industrial purposes. Major confidential sponsored research projects have been concerned with development of a cellulose preparation for producing glucose from bagasse, development of specific thermostable polysaccharases for upgrading animal feedstuffs by enzyme supplementation, production of fungal protein from waste cereal, characterization of soils by quantitative estimation of their enzyme activities, development of an automated method for the quantitative estimation of soluble blood group substances in saliva, and investigation of the biodegradability of industrial chemicals and their toxicity to micro-organisms found in effluent treatment plants.

In the past two decades there has been heightened public recognition of the finiteness of the raw material and energy resources of this planet. This has led many industries to explore ways of modifying their production processes so as to minimize pollution and the use of non-renewable materials. In line with this thinking, Shirley's biotechnology research programme includes projects on the elaboration of biopolymers from micro-organisms which offer possibilities for such uses as sizes, print thickeners, stiffening agents, and adhesives; the development of microbially derived pigments; and the development of biosurfactants, as a biodegradable alternative to conventional detergents.

Environmental Sciences

High health and safety standards in the workplace are the rightful expectation of all employees, and in the UK and other advanced countries maintenance of these standards is increasingly being given the backing of legislation. Shirley supports the textile industry by providing a comprehensive monitoring service dealing with noise, dust, toxic fumes and gases, asbestos, water and effluents. A range of testing equipment and specialized techniques are used.

Shirley also advises industry on the supply, handling, and disposal of any material, to comply with current statutory requirements and recommended procedures. Close links are maintained with the Health and Safety Executive and other appropriate Government Departments.

In the early 1980s the Institute's Biotechnology group conducted a major research project on byssinosis, a disease which can affect textile workers handling cotton, flax, hemp, and sisal. There is a large body of evidence

Dr M.J. Hewson conducting a dust survey in a mill.

relating the prevalence of this lung condition to dust concentration, although the exact causative mechanism has not so far been discovered. The Shirley study, carried out in collaboration with a medical research team, involved analysis of airborne matter associated with byssinosis, and investigated possible causes and means of prevention of the disease.

Machinery noise can also affect workers adversely, leading to hearing impairment, and there are therefore restrictions on the level and duration of exposure to noise in the workplace. The Institute's monitoring service for noise and dust in industrial premises helps firms to stay below the permitted maximum levels.

Shirley also offers advice on the avoidance of toxic hazards arising from process chemicals and from atmospheric gases and vapours. A pollutant of current concern is formaldehyde, a chemical widely used in textile finishing, which can irritate the upper respiratory tract and cause dermatitis in susceptible persons. Institute surveys of a large number of clothing factories and industrial workrooms have provided a considerable mass of data on the types of textile-handling process where problems are likely to occur. On the basis of this experience and the perceived industrial need for an effective, portable monitoring device, the Institute has recently developed an instrument for the measurement of released formaldehyde, which is at present undergoing trials prior to commercial launch. The "Shirley" Formaldemeter provides a rapid instrumental method of determining formaldehyde release from textiles, or from any other formaldehyde-based resin-finished product.

Forensic investigations, and associated expert witness, form a large part of the work of the Environmental Sciences staff, assisted by the facilities and investigative expertise of other sections of the Institute, notably the Shirley Testing Service (see below).

Specialized Analytical Services

Instrumental methods of analysis of textiles and other materials are widely used in the Institute's research and technical service work. A service is offered relating to the applications of colour physics, for dye recipe prediction and correction, assessment of colour match acceptability, colour sorting, and determination of the limits of control required over processing variables.

A multi-client research project on fabric yellowing has yielded important information on the range of causative mechanisms involved, on the basis of which ways of preventing this costly industrial problem are being developed.

However, recent years have seen an increase in the demand for investigations requiring the use of sophisticated equipment for the instrumental analysis of chemical composition, including chromatography (gas-liquid, thin-layer, high-performance liquid), ultraviolet and visible spectrophotometry, and infrared spectroscopy.

The majority of the clients for these services are small and medium-sized firms, and much of the work requires innovative solutions and development of new test methods to suit individual needs. An example of such service work is a special testing procedure to assess the efficiency of commercial washing powders and liquids, devised for a large international manufacturer.

Microelectronics, Instrumentation, Engineering

Accurate measurement of processing variables and product behaviour is an essential facilitating step towards their objective evaluation, which is in turn a prerequisite to improvement or modification of textile materials.

Since its early days Shirley has designed and developed testing instruments, many of which are now well established commercially for use at all stages of textile processing. Mechanical and electronic devices are now being superseded by sophisticated microcomputer and transputer systems, and Shirley staff have been in the forefront of the application of the developing technology to the textile industry.

Process monitoring and control are an important aspect of the microelectronics work at Shirley, an example of this being hardware and software for spinning and winding installations designed and constructed for an industrial client in a collaboration over several years.

Members of the Cotton Industry War Memorial Trust on a visit to the Institute, 1987.

"Shirley" Processor Board, developed in the microelectronics workroom, for use in specialized control and measurement equipment for the textile industry.

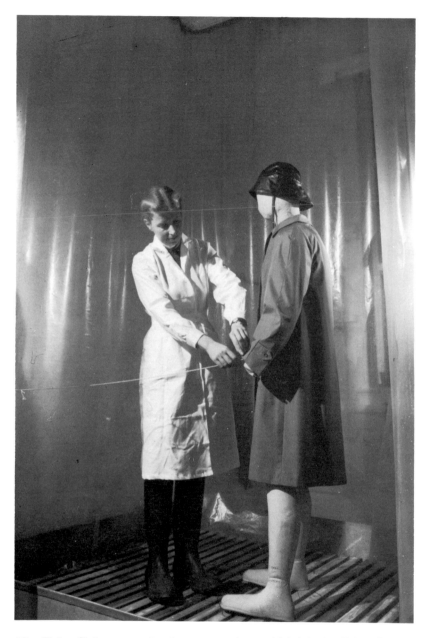

Miss Elaine Clulow measuring the waterproofness of fabric in the Shirley Rain Room.

As to current projects, an image analysis system for the objective assessment of pilling and creasing in fabrics has reached prototype stage. The microelectronics staff were also involved in final refinements to the "Shirley" Formaldemeter (described above).

Work on new and improved instruments is an ongoing part of Shirley's activities, in particular, upgrading of established instruments to incorporate microprocessor technology.

Many of the instruments initiated in the Shirley laboratories have subsequently become widely available through Shirley Developments Limited (formerly an offshoot of the Institute but now an independent company, as described elsewhere in this book). In recent years the Institute's microelectronics and engineering staff have taken responsibility for the manufacture of certain instruments, on a routine basis, on behalf of Shirley Developments.

There has been an Engineering Department at Shirley since the very early days, and, as described elsewhere, most of the testing and laboratory equipment used to be purpose-built on the premises. Nowadays that is no longer a sensible or economic option for standard items of equipment. However, the Engineering Workroom provides specialized engineering services both to the other sections of the Institute and to industry, including design of new instruments, instrument repair and manufacture, adaptation of standard equipment for clients' own requirements, and manufacture of prototypes associated with new products and processes.

A recent innovatory product, the "Shirley" Safety Knife for use in industry, has now been licensed to an industrial company for commercial exploitation. This is one of several projects linked to the health and welfare of textile workers, arising from the fruitful long-term collaboration between Shirley and the Cotton Industry War Memorial Trust; other such items in preparation are a low-cost cumulative noise dosimeter, and a face mask to minimize dust inhalation. (It is noteworthy that in the Institute's first crucial ten years, 1920-1930, this Fund provided 47% of the money to finance the research programme, as compared with 17% from Government, and 36% from trade subscriptions.)

The Engineering consultancy service specializes in problems of heat transfer, fluid mechanics, and control engineering.

Shirley Testing Service

A multi-disciplinary approach to textile testing and trouble-shooting is adopted by the Shirley Testing Service. Prior to 1972 (the year the statutory levy ceased) its work was exclusively for Member firms. However, since that pivotal date a much wider customer-base has been established and is constantly being extended, both in terms of numbers of clients and the diversity of topics dealt with. A brochure listing all the tests offered was published in 1972, and at irregular intervals since then. In 1972 a total of 185

Training course on Fibre Identification, conducted by Mrs M. Greeves.

different tests were listed; the August 1988 edition offers 480 tests.

Often the confidence built up through regular use of the routine testing service has led companies to "come to Shirley" when the need arose for more complex or longer-term investigations.

A major landmark in the expansion of the service came in January 1986 when Shirley was successful in its application for NATLAS accreditation for a large number of its tests. This step involved refurbishment of the physical and chemical testing laboratories and the creation of a quality system based upon principles similar to those of BS 5750 for the operations of manufacturing and service industries. The system has a management structure with continuous monitoring and recording of checks on calibration of equipment, test procedures, sample handling and reporting of test results. Regular independent assessments are also made. The National Testing Laboratory Accreditation Scheme was later renamed NAMAS (National Measurement Accreditation Service), and Shirley's accreditation as NAMAS Testing Laboratory No. 0435 assures clients of the quality of the workmanship in conducting the tests listed in its NAMAS Schedule.

After even the first few months of operation, the time and cost invested in setting up the system were yielding benefits, both in day-to-day working efficiency and in attracting still more business.

During the year 1986-7 Shirley set up a testing service for geotextiles, the high-strength, heavy-duty fabrics and membranes used in civil engineering. With its thorough knowledge of textiles, its existing test facilities, and the recent addition of a 200 kN tensile tester, the Institute offers specialist expertise in geotextiles and is currently developing a range of tests derived from both the textile and soil-mechanics disciplines. There is close liaison with the UK Government's Department of Transport, the British Standards Institution, and other interested parties.

Technical Economy

During the past two decades, the services under the general heading of Technical Economy have been extended from Shirley Members only to a worldwide clientele, ranging from companies involved in all aspects of textile trade and production to firms considering diversification into textiles. This was one of the first Institute departments to actively seek contract work from overseas clients, thus spearheading Shirley's development from a local into an international organization.

A wide range of techno-economic and market surveys has been carried out, on topics as diverse as car seat belts, measuring instruments, production management software, and new end-uses for polypropylene fibre. These services have been provided for UK firms considering expansion into overseas markets, and for overseas companies wishing to assess the suitability of their products for European and UK markets; existing products or innovative items may be involved, and much of the work is highly commercially sensitive.

A substantial amount of work has been done for overseas Governments, and has included studies of discrete industry sectors or the whole of a country's textile industry where rehabilitation or restructuring is required; often international aid agencies such as the World Bank and the United Nations Industrial Development Organization (UNIDO) have provided the funding for such projects.

Training courses and conferences

Shirley began to run formal training courses and conferences for industry personnel in 1963. The move was stimulated by the Government's initiative in setting up the Industry Training Boards (ITBs), with the aim of increasing the quantity and quality of trained staff in UK industry and thereby improving its international competitiveness.

In about one-third of the courses offered, skills and knowledge are imparted in such a way as to prepare trainees for their application to specific jobs, e.g. fibre identification, physical and chemical analyses, and other laboratory functions. The remaining courses concentrate on knowledge acquisition without manual skills, either at introductory level, or at "post-advanced" level. The introductory courses are designed to give supervisory and trainee management personnel an insight into the structure and methods of the textile or clothing industries, through talks and demonstrations of production machinery. The post-advanced courses are intended for responsible, experienced managerial and technical staff, to provide mid-career training in what is to them an unfamiliar branch of textile technology; these courses are usually termed "workshops" and a valuable feature is a concluding open forum to which the participants can contribute.

One of the original, and continuing, aims of Shirley conferences and courses is the transfer of recent R&D results and laboratory methods to industry. Additionally such events, the larger conferences in particular, are forums for interchange of ideas between the industry's technologists, and are an opportunity for state-of-the-art presentations on a specific narrow subject, as for instance in 1988 "Polyester Textiles".

The subject-matter of Shirley training courses (which do not encompass operative training) is designed to complement the programmes offered by universities, further education establishments, private training contractors, and industry itself.

Two specific areas are worthy of highlighting. The course entitled "Introduction to Textiles", dealing with the properties and behaviour of fibres, yarns, and fabrics, is held several times a year and continues to be much in demand. Trainees are attracted not only from the textile and clothing industries, but from companies such as retailers who have a commercial interest in the industries' products. A second important area is the provision of management courses and consultancy on "Quality Systems", particularly appropriate in view of the requirements of BS 5750 (equivalent to ISO 9000-4) with which an increasing number of firms have decided to comply. Though such compliance is not mandatory, UK Government Departments and other major buyers of textiles are insisting that firms with which they now do business must have a BS 5750 quality assurance scheme in place.

Information Services

The research workers at Shirley, and thus the clients they serve, have ready access to the world's textile literature – articles in trade and learned periodicals, patents, books, reviews, conference papers – through "World Textile Abstracts" and associated computer-based data retrieval services. Today's information systems at the Institute have their roots in the "Summary of Current Literature", a publication started in the 1920s for the benefit of the staff – who were then largely scientists unfamiliar with the details of textile processes – and soon made available to Member firms. Since that date information scientists at Shirley have prepared summaries of virtually all the technical and scientific items published which are relevant to textiles. Since the service was computerized some 20 years ago, the abstracts are entered into the "World Textiles" database for international access, and are also published in printed form.

The Shirley Publications series, which has now reached No. 51, consists of monographs issued from time to time, on diverse themes; some are sets of Shirley conference papers, others literature reviews on specific topics. The series started in 1972, and was successor to two earlier series, the Confidential Pamphlets, intended for mill managers, and the Shirley Institute Memoirs, scientific papers which were often also published in the Journal of the Textile Institute.

The periodical "Textiles" was started in 1965 with the title "The Shirley Link" and launched under its present title in 1972. It provides general background information on fibres, yarns, and fabrics, their production and properties, and has a broadly educational purpose. It has built up an international readership both in the textile and allied industries and amongst textile teachers in school and colleges.

The Institute has always had an obligation to disseminate to the industry the results of the research projects undertaken with Government support. In addition to verbal communications (liaison visits, informal seminars, conferences and courses), this has been done over the years by means of several regular publications for Members, principally Shirley Institute Bulletin, Director's Research Report, and the Annual Report & Accounts, as well as various occasional leaflets and brochures.

As already mentioned by Mr Tippett in his account of the first 50 years, the "Shirley Institute Bulletin" was established for Members in 1928, as a forum for exchange of ideas between the mill man and the scientist. The Bulletin continued until 1987, although it has been necessary since the 1970s, because much of the work has been confidential to clients, to permit only limited release of technical information.

With the need to maximize fee-earning activity in the last two decades, considerable effort has been directed to publicizing Shirley work more widely in order to attract industrial sponsors; a large number of press releases, leaflets, and brochures has been produced by the Information Services staff, and much of this output has also been printed in-house.

Maureen Sawbridge

Chapter V
Then and Now

Then

The foregoing pages have recorded something of the changes in the political and economic environment within which, over the years, Shirley Institute has conducted its work and they have given an insight into the constraints within which it has had to operate. These controlling parameters have changed markedly with time. And so, too, has the life and feel of the place as experienced by the "insider".

The Institute grew to full maturity during the 20s, 30s, and 40s, in what one might describe as an almost Victorian atmosphere engendered by strong paternal management from the top and an array of established practices, customs, and social etiquette derived from academia and from more elegant days. The two early Directors were men of considerable authority and distinction: Dr A.W. Crossley, CMG, CBE, FRS (1920-1926) and Sir Robert Pickard, FRS, DSc (1927-1943). They directed the Institute during its flowering years when its reputation reached a very high level, both nationally and internationally, in cotton and cellulose science and technology.

Sir Robert was very much a Victorian-type character: an established national figure, confident and strongly assertive of his authority and control, crusty yet paternal and protective in his regard for his staff (as long as people did as they were told!).

He commanded (the right verb) a staff whose main component was a body of extremely well-qualified scientists, many of whom had gained first-class degrees at leading British universities and, as an encore, PhDs and/or DScs at prestigious German universities. Since, in those days, there was little employment opportunity for scientists outside the confines of universities, it was not difficult for the Institute to recruit such high-calibre people. The mix of firm direction from Sir Robert and the character and ability of an erudite though sometimes contentious scientific staff resulted in a life of not-inconsiderable tension and much excitement, a life that engendered high achievement and the establishment of a sound scientific and technical basis for the cotton textile industry. It should be said, however, that part of this achievement resulted from the fact that the industry was largely based on craft skill and empirical knowledge and was, therefore, scientifically unexplored territory, presenting an almost virgin field for the work of the Institute's scientists.

In addition to strong leadership and a well qualified scientific staff, a further factor contributing to the development of the Institute's reputation was the enthusiasm and talents of both the technical staff and the assistant staff. Today, distinctions between different levels and types of staff have become diffuse and of little note as a guide to the quality of an organization. But in the 20s, 30s, and even into the 40s, distinctions and barriers were built into the operational and social structure of very many organizations, and certainly were in the case of Shirley. The technical staff were largely recruited from the operatives, technicians, and managers of the Lancashire textile industry, people who brought to the Institute the rich dialects of the county, the practical knowledge of the cotton industry and its processes, and a blunt pride in their own abilities. The assistant staff were recruited from a now-defunct labour pool: bright young school-leavers of 15 or so years of age, most of whom were keen to develop their abilities and qualifications by working in a disciplined and prestigious laboratory whilst, at the same time, pursuing part-time studies at local colleges. For very many young people, this was their only option in acquiring a higher education and, in time, many of these assistants gained degrees such as external London University BScs, MScs and PhDs; some remained for a lifetime in the Institute's service.

The three main types of staff, scientists, technologists, and laboratory assistants, were effectively maintained as separate social and status streams not unlike those of the armed forces with officers, NCOs, and other ranks. There was a tendency to consider the scientists to be people with highly academic minds, minds that were uncluttered with the detail of technical processes and machinery: it was the technologists who should be concerned with such "non-intellectual" matters. The laboratory assistants were carefully trained and were worked hard in the conduct of a wide variety of experiments and tests: they produced the data which assisted the technologists or on which the scientists brooded and theorized. One can now look back with wry amusement to note that if a laboratory assistant eventually acquired a part-time degree or other high qualification then he would most likely   be promoted into the technical rather than the scientific grades. In those days in Britain, and certainly in the Institute, science considered itself somewhat "above" technology and believed that those whose minds had not been trained by full-time university education were unlikely to become true scientists.

However, despite what in cold print might seem to be an uneasy system of social and organizational stratification, relations between all members of staff were good, usually friendly and cheerful; activity was always high because it was spurred by the general belief in the great value of scientific and technical enquiry and the high dignity attained by the conduct of such work. Not-infrequent visits by Royalty, eminent industrialists, and distinguished scientists such as Sir Lawrence Bragg heightened the feeling of being involved in very important work. The occasionally eccentric behaviour of some of the more senior staff (for example, one man could think best in hot weather with his bare feet in a basin of cold water) added piquancy to life.

A fourth determinant of the Institute's daily lifestyle was the personality of one man who held a dominant position at the centre of affairs: that of the laboratory steward. His name was Mr Sturgess, with an emphasis very much on the "Mr". He had retired from the regular army as a sergeant major, but never really retired from his rank and the ambience of authority. He controlled the issue of all supplies and materials to the staff and also had charge of the laboratory assistants for the first half hour or so of each day for the cleaning and polishing of their laboratory (barrack) rooms. His personality demanded instant action even by quite senior staff: it ensured that laboratories, benches, and glassware were always kept immaculate (Sir Robert Pickard was himself rather keen that this should be so); and it ensured materials and equipment were issued and used on a most frugal basis. Thus, a request for the replacement of a pencil of not more than half an inch in length might, albeit reluctantly, be granted but a request for the replacement of a blunt and much-worn pair of scissors was likely to be met by stern outrage.

A typical day's routine in this highly motivated but closely regulated environment started at 8.30 a.m., with the laboratory assistants diligently (especially in the vicinity of Mr Sturgess) cleaning benches and polishing glassware. At about 9.00 a.m. the technical staff, and at about 9.15 a.m. the more senior staff would start arriving. The senior staff's arrival and departure times were rather variable because many of them did much of their report writing at home and there was also the belief that minds engaged on "higher things" could not be switched on or off at fixed times of the day. Since, in general, each laboratory was occupied by one or two senior staff plus up to six laboratory assistants attached to each, laboratory working space was at a premium. Any recording and other writing that had to be done was accomplished in the elbows-tucked-in position on about 2ft width of bench. Similarly, experimental equipment such as viscometry tanks occupied fairly cramped space. The laboratory assistants generally had quite extensive programmes of measuring or testing work to conduct and would work under their own steam for several days before reporting results to their seniors. The latter would be occupied with the first-time setting up of new experiments or devices, with calculating (very many hours were spent cranking the handles of mechanical calculating machines!), or with initial report drafting. But senior staff also spent much time away from their laboratories, since discussions with colleagues, reporting to a Head of Department, meeting visitors, routine library reading of the scientific and technical literature, attending committee meetings and seminars, and the like all occupied much more time than in today's more hurried world.

Most laboratory assistants attended college for one whole day plus one or two evenings each week; in addition each assistant was allowed half-a-day per week of free time, usually spent in the Library, to copy up and revise college notes. In contrast to today, the Library was therefore usually crowded,

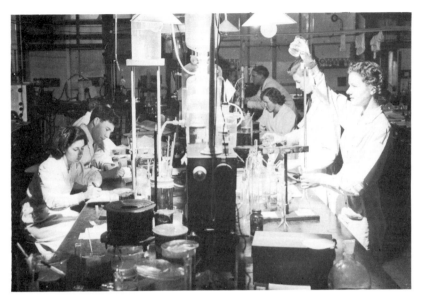

Then . . .

with laboratory assistants who remained in their lab coats and senior staff who now wore just their suits, a nice distinction between staff levels.

Friday afternoons were generally reserved for waxing and polishing laboratory benches (senior staff made themselves scarce like husbands on a wash day) and Saturday mornings were reserved for the more leisurely completion of tasks left over from week-day work.

One social nicety of those days was the partaking of afternoon tea—not the quick individual cuppa of today but the formal assembly of senior staff for tea, cakes, and learned discussion in the staff dining room. Although such a practice would be far too wasteful of time nowadays, the daily assemblies had the beneficial effect of keeping senior staff in close touch with each other's work and thoughts, and engendered the feeling of close community.

Male staff members universally addressed one another by their surnames but were always careful to preface the surname by a "Mr" or "Dr", as appropriate. Mr Sturgess played safe by addressing all the more senior staff members as "Dr" which brought a quiet blush of pride to many a "Mr". Christian names, even between laboratory assistants, were unused and female staff and assistants were always given the courteous prefix of "Miss".

What of the work itself? First of all, high accuracy of measurement was demanded, with much replication to ensure reliability of results. This demand for accuracy resulted in tediously long "runs" of measurement which today would be hopelessly expensive. The chemist largely relied on his own "craft" tools: balance weights, pipettes, measuring flasks, burettes and the like, all personally calibrated and frequently re-checked, and on a range of standard solutions which themselves demanded much effort in making up and calibration. Pretty well all the glassware used was "blown" by the Institute's glassblowers: this included not only volume-measuring glassware such as pipettes and flasks but also viscometers, distillation apparatus, conical flasks, and weighing bottles. The physicist largely relied on fairly basic mechanical, electrical, and other equipment put together in the laboratory, sometimes with the assistance of the engineering workshops. A particular feature of much of this equipment was the incorporation of numerous Meccano parts. This occurred not only at the Institute but also in many other laboratories, yet the great contribution of Meccano to the march of science in the 30s, 40s and 50s has received scant recognition!

The clean-living and theoretically oriented physicists were often at odds with their more "earthy" chemical colleagues because of the noxious smells produced by the latter in the course of their work (in those days, chemists were less safety or environmentally conscious): the sudden appearance of a red-faced physicist in a chemical laboratory to complain volubly about the "stink" of pyridine or other noxious agents was just part of normal life.

The long hours spent in the conduct of experiments and measurements were matched only by the time spent in the drafting, writing, and rewriting of reports and papers. Extensive publication in Institute, learned society and other journals was very important to the reputation of both the organization and its individual staff members, and was a feature of Institute policy.

First-draft papers and articles were always prepared on the backs of old galley proofs to avoid wasteful use of virgin paper. After typing, the drafts were scrutinized by at least two Institute referees for accuracy, clarity, and, in particular, the good use of English. This procedure led to referees' comments (also recorded on the back of old galley proofs) which were not infrequently more voluminous than the original subject matter! Having surmounted the internal refereeing hurdle, the paper was edited in the Institute's Information Department and then submitted to yet more, external, referees. Looking back one often marvels at how so much was published in the face of so many human obstacles, for there was indeed a great stream of published papers.

As to the non-work interests of the staff, they were then, as now, very varied. Many excelled in do-it-yourself activities long before DIY became a national preoccupation and were extremely inventive. In the late 40s and early 50s when cars were in very short supply, the vehicles of the Institute's staff ran the roads long after their natural lives had ended and it was always a remarkable sight to see life being breathed (sometimes with difficulty) into a collection of mechanical geriatrics at the end of each working day. One member of staff, sadly recently deceased, developed his garden round an automatic mowing principle. His lawns consisted of interlocking circles of grass each with a central pin position. The motor mower was set in motion after being attached to a central pin by a cord. As it described circles round the pin it was slowly wound to the centre of the circle! The operation would be repeated on the next overlapping circle. Magic!

Social events were conducted with great formality and decorum. The annual Christmas Ball was attended by every senior staff member irrespective of dancing ability or social inclination, all in full evening dress of varying antiquity, usually completed by white gloves. Alcohol was never served on such occasions. Dances were led off by the partnership of senior ladies and gentlemen as determined by order of status and seniority. But with the war years these strict conventions started to crumble.

Institute sporting teams were produced along similar lines. Sir Robert Pickard was himself a keen and able sportsman, as were many of his senior staff. Consequently it required considerable ability for a more junior member of staff to achieve a place in a team composed mainly of Directors and Heads of Department!

One aspect of life at Shirley in the 30s, 40s and 50s reflects the formality of the times: all forms of socializing between members of the opposite sex were greatly frowned upon, particularly between junior members of staff. The possibility of enticements was stamped out at an early stage, for example the senior (in years and seasoning) female scientist had the (official? unofficial?) duty of ensuring that female laboratory assistants behaved "properly", wore no form of lipstick or make-up (otherwise "Go to the cloakroom, Miss Burkinshaw, and clean your face"!), and were soberly presented and attired.

What can one say in comparing "then" with "now"? Both lifestyles were/are products of their time, governed by social conventions, attitudes to work, the valuation placed on fundamental research, the extent of financial pressures, and the nature of general government and industrial policies.

Then, assistant labour was relatively cheap and freely available and this, plus the use of inexpensive, simple and long-lasting equipment, enabled long-term experimental work to be conducted at not too high a cost. Furthermore, properly directed research work offered the likelihood of results of significant scientific value. Since everyone was working to provide a basic scientific understanding in a long-established but largely empirical industry, all had a straightforward objective and it was sufficient to know that research was of value just for being "research". Each scientist coming to work at the Institute, within a relatively short space of time, began to develop a specialized interest in a narrow field of study which, in many instances, became a lifetime's endeavour. Thus, in time, the Institute's senior staff came to consist largely of narrow-field experts and each was willing to share this deep expertise and knowledge with colleagues.

So, overall, life at Shirley has changed in the last 40 or so years from the relatively steady but rewarding pursuit of knowledge for its own sake to rapid pursuit of the latest technology for immediate industrial application and profit in a highly competitive environment. Nowadays, all members of staff have to do their best to earn their own "corn" in a very real sense.

One wonders what changes the next 40 or so years will bring.

Reg Cumberbirch

. . . and Now

Fifty years ago it was easy for the Institute to engage top-quality staff. At that time the opportunities to carry out academic research at University were reserved for the brilliant few; DSIR grants, which opened up the postgraduate research world, did not become widely available until the early 1960s. Places like Shirley Institute offered an excellent alternative, since the work was still both intellectually demanding and scientifically interesting, and time could be devoted exclusively to the pursuit of knowledge. Today, research organizations have to compete on unfavourable terms with the lucrative appointments offered by an increasingly technological industry. Consequently, there is very little recruitment to Shirley from industry, and such as there is occurs mainly at senior levels for the import of particular expertise.

The extension of availability of university places which followed the Robbins Committee report of the early 60s has resulted in a considerable reduction in the pool of science-based school-leavers who would normally have sought employment as laboratory assistants, and also of those who would have become craft apprentices. This levelling of standards has inevitably resulted in a change of perception and expectation of what is wanted from a graduate technologist. He or she is expected to carry out all the tasks, of necessity, which an unqualified assistant once carried out. The distinction between "scientists" and "technologists" has tended to disappear over recent years as the cost of employing experts in each particular subject has become prohibitive. Nowadays, a research worker has to be not only a "jack-of-all-trades" but also a *master* as well!

The breakdown of social and academic distinctions over the last thirty years or so has resulted in a workforce where junior members do not feel intimidated when talking to senior staff and vice versa. It is not considered undignified for senior staff to talk with juniors, whether junior in years or in status. But there are still residues of the old styles and courtesies; and best reflected in the uncertainties in use of titles, Christian names or surnames. In addition, the operation of the Institute on a commercial footing has exposed staff to some of the previously unconsidered aspects of working for cash. The threats to security of employment which members of staff then felt strongly resulted in staff representation finally through an affiliated Trade Union, with that representation applying to all grades of staff. It is difficult under these circumstances to maintain levels of aloofness within the same organization. Such a corporate activity could not have been understood by Sir Robert Pickard.

Working conditions have changed with the advent of flexible working hours catering for the unpredictability of research work and for modern social

. . . and Now.

requirements. The 9 a.m. to 5.30 p.m. working-day is virtually extinct with many members of staff preferring an early start and finish. It is not uncommon, however, to see (senior) employees leaving well after the official end of the day (6 p.m.) and taking work home.

While the self-imposed standards of laboratory discipline would appear today a relic of another era, they undoubtedly acted as a yardstick of performance and quality, against which many of today's standards of cleanliness and tidiness would fall short. The self-imposed standards of the past have now been replaced by a national standard, that of NAMAS accreditation, and the discipline now is not self-determined, but accompanied by a threat of public disgrace, with consequent and inevitable loss of business.

This is a necessary counter to the commercial pressure now placed on a workforce who have to account in writing for all their time; now it is unacceptable for laboratory staff to be "unproductive" for 20% of the working week. Readily available sources of glassware have resulted in the attitude that flasks, etc., are now consumable items, that is, it costs more, in terms of staff productive time, to clean out a badly soiled flask than to buy a new article. Formal gatherings of staff at tea and coffee breaks are also prohibitively expensive, although unofficial laboratory breaks are common.

Modern analytical techniques, with increasing   reliance on instrumentation, have taken away much of the drudgery of time-consuming repetitive analyses. Additionally, techniques that were undreamt of fifty years ago are now available to the scientist. However, in this microchip-reliant age there is still room for innovation and ingenuity and for the "home-made" piece of apparatus to perform an out-of-the-ordinary task.

One major difference between then and now is the vast improvement in information technology. Computer-based data storage and retrieval have virtually done away with manual literature searches; armed with appropriate keywords the scientist can quickly amass a list of all relevant references to a particular topic, be they in Japanese, Russian, or the more understandable, European, languages. Unfortunately, reading them all still takes a long time!

The huge advances in communications mean that the researcher can now talk to clients worldwide, and send or receive facsimile copies of papers or reports within minutes using the fax facility. The end result is a wider market, rapid dissemination of information, and a better service to the busy client.

In essence, therefore, the spur and discipline of the cost/benefit ratio have replaced the pursuit of scientific knowledge for its own sake; nowadays there is almost always a commercial goal. One of these goals has, funnily enough, been the deliberate development of "smells", albeit latent noxious aromas for the sensory early warning of hazardous events such as fires.

Anthony Sagar

Appendix 1

Members of the Council of BCIRA, March 1921

Chairman.
Mr Kenneth Lee, Messrs Tootal Broadhurst Lee Co. Ltd.

Vice-Chairmen.
Mr H.R. Armitage, Bradford Dyers' Association Ltd., and Employers' Federation of Dyers & Finishers.
Mr W. Greenwood, MP., Federation of Master Cotton Spinners' Associations Ltd.
Mr Forrest Hewit, Federation of Calico Printers.

Vice-Chairman and Hon. Treasurer.
Mr A.W. Heyworth, Messrs. Eli Heyworth & Sons Ltd.

Dr W.L. Balls, Fine Cotton Spinners' and Doublers' Association.
Mr T.D. Barlow, Barlow and Jones Ltd.
Mr J.W. Baron, Boardman and Baron Ltd.
Mr F.W. Barwick, Manchester Chamber of Commerce Testing House.
Mr H. Boothman, Amalgamated Association of Operative Cotton Spinners.
Mr S. Bourne, Nottingham Chamber of Commerce.
Mr G. Burrows, The Stockport Belgrave Ltd.
Mr H.W. Christie, The United Turkey Red Co. Ltd.
Mr Vernon Clay, Employers' Federation of Dyers and Finishers.
Mr Harold Cliff, Federation of Master Cotton Spinners' Associations.
Mr J. Crinion, Card & Blowing Room Operatives' Associations.
Mr W.H. Dixon, Federation of Calico Printers.
Mr E. Dyson, English Velvet and Cord Dyers' Association.
Mr W. Fell, Cotton Spinners' and Manufacturers' Association.
Mr H.P. Greg, R. Greg and Co. Ltd.
Mr A.E. Hawley, Leicester Chamber of Commerce.
Mr W. Heaps, Federation of Master Cotton Spinners' Associations.
Mr S.H. Higgins, Bleachers' Association Ltd.
Sir John H. Holden, Bart., Tunnicliffe and Hampson (1920) Ltd., Bedford and Mill Lane Spinning Co. (1920) Ltd. Alder Spinning Co. Ltd.
Mr J.H. Lester, Tootai Broadhurst Lee Co. Ltd.
Mr W. Lloyd, Operative Bleachers', Dyers' and Finishers' Association (Bolton Amalgamation).
Mr W.H. Pennington, Burgess, Ledward and Co. Ltd.
Mr H. Roberts, Federation of Master Cotton Spinners' Associations.
Mr Ed. E. Shaw, Cotton Spinners' and Manufacturers' Association.
Mr F.J. Smith, British Cotton and Wool Dyers' Association Ltd.
Mr C. Speak, Amalgamated Weavers' Association.
Mr H. Taylor, Federation of Master Cotton Spinners' Associations.

Appendix 2

Chairmen, Directors, and Secretaries, 1919-88

Chairmen of Shirley Institute

Mr H.R. Armitage (1919)
Sir Kenneth Lee (1919-29)
Mr T. Nuttall (1929-30)
Mr H.P. Greg (1930-33)
Mr H.S. Butterworth (1933-45)
Sir Harold Parkinson OBE, JP (1945-49)
Mr N.G. McCulloch CBE (1949-60)
Mr J. Lindley OBE JP (1960, died in office)
Sir Cuthbert Clegg TD, JP, MA (1961-62)
Mr G.H Jolly (1962-65)
Mr J.H. Spencer OBE (1965-71)
Dr P.W. Smith OBE (1971-88)

Directors of Shirley Institute

1920-27 Dr A.W. Crossley, CMG, CBE, FRS

1927-43 Dr (Sir) Robert H. Pickard, FRS

1943-55 Dr F.C. Toy, CBE

1955-69 Dr D.W. Hill, CBE

1969-80 Mr L.A. Wiseman, OBE

1980-81 Mr K.A. Mitchell (Chief Executive)

1980-82 Dr J. Honeyman (Director of Research)

1982-88 Dr A. Maclean (Managing Director)

Company Secretaries of BCIRA/Shirley

1920-51 Mr Charles Packer
1951-79 Mr Kenneth E. Lewis
1979-86 Mr Reg E. Ranby-Hutcheon
1986-88 Mr Albert Lawless

Chairmen of BRRA

Sir William Palmer (1947-56)
Mr Ivan C.Hill (1956-61)

Directors of BRRA

Mr J. Wilson MC, MSc, FRIC (1946-1957)
Mr L.A. Wiseman OBE, BSc, ARIC, FTI (1957-1961)

Company Secretary of BRRA

Mr H.B. Gee (1947-61)

Appendix 3

Biographical notes on Directors of Research.

Dr A.W. Crossley, CMG, CBE, FRS

Arthur William Crossley was born in Accrington, Lancs in 1869. He was educated at Mill Hill School and then at Owens College (later the University of Manchester), where he gained an Honours degree in Chemistry. He subsequently worked for his PhD at Wurzburg, followed by study at Berlin, returning in 1894 to research work at Manchester, and then at St Thomas's Hospital, London. He was appointed Daniell Professor of Chemistry at King's College London in 1914. During the first World War he was responsible for setting up the chemical warfare research establishment at Porton Down, for the development of both offensive and defensive systems for the army. The French Government created him an Officier de la Légion d'Honneur for his advisory work during the War, and he was awarded the CMG in 1917 and the CBE in 1919. Dr Crossley was appointed first Director of Shirley Institute in 1919, and succeeded in recruiting a team of high quality staff and establishing the laboratories within two years. However, the strenuous work of the wartime period had weakened his constitution and he died at the early age of 58 in 1927.

Sir Robert Pickard, FRS

Robert Howson Pickard was born in Birmingham and educated at King Edward's Grammar School and at Mason College (later Birmingham University) where he obtained his PhD. He went on to study at London and Munich Universities. In 1899 he was appointed head of the Chemistry Department at Blackburn Technical College, and in 1907 principal of the College. He became principal of Battersea Polytechnic in 1919. In 1927 on the death of Dr Crossley he was invited to become Director of Shirley Institute, a post he held until the end of 1943. Sir Robert was a past president of the Royal Institute of Chemistry and of the Society of Chemical Industry, and was director of, and for many years adviser to, the British Leather Manufacturers Research Association. He was Vice-Chancellor of London University (1937-39) and for many years Chairman of Convocation. He was elected FRS in 1917 and knighted in 1937. Sir Robert died in October 1948, aged seventy-six years.

Dr F.C. Toy, CBE

Francis Carter Toy was born in Helston, Cornwall in 1892. After education at Launceston College, he graduated (BSc 1914, MSc 1920, DSc 1922) at University College London. War service in France was followed by ten years as Chief Physicist at the British Photographic Research Association (1919-29). He was appointed Deputy Director of the Shirley Institute in 1930 and succeeded Sir Robert Pickard as Director in 1943. He retired in 1955, and lives in Wilmslow, Cheshire, now aged 96. Dr Toy is a Fellow of the Textile Institute. He has been President of a number of organizations, including the Institute of Physics, the Manchester Statistical Society, and the Manchester Literary and Philosophical Society.

Dr D.W. Hill, CBE

Douglas William Hill, a native of Bristol, graduated in Chemistry at Bristol University; he gained his PhD at Liverpool University and then spent three years as Commonwealth Research Fellow at the University of Illinois and the Rockefeller Institute for Medical Research in New York. After subsequent teaching experience at Bristol and Exeter Universities, and research at the University of Bonn, he joined the Shirley staff in 1937. During World War II he was seconded to the Ministry of Supply and Combined Production and Resources Board in Washington, DC, USA, returning to Shirley as Deputy Director in 1944. He succeeded Dr Toy in 1955, and retired in 1969. In 1965 he was awarded the CBE; he was made an Honorary Fellow of the Textile Institute in 1960; Hon. Life Member of TI in 1969. As Chairman of the Board of Governors of the Royal College of Advanced Technology, Salford, Dr Hill was a leading figure in the setting up of its chartered successor, the University of Salford, in 1967, being appointed Pro-Chancellor at that date; he was awarded an Hon. DSc of University of Salford in 1969. Dr Hill died on 16th May 1985.

Mr J. Wilson, CBE, MC, MSc, FRIC, Director, BRRA.

John Wilson, the founder Director of the British Rayon Research Association, was born in 1890 and died in September 1976. During this period, he achieved so much because of his inexhaustible energy, his own ability, an unwavering belief in science, a respect for good scientists and the capacity to attract them to work for him.

The first part of his career can be said to start in 1908 when he entered teaching, proceeding through a series of schools until he became science lecturer at the Borough Polytechnic, London. Military service during 1914-1919, when he served with great distinction (Military Cross and bar, gassed twice, wounded three times), was followed by two years' study at Sheffield University, after which he was awarded a first-class Honours degree in Chemistry, followed by an MSc for one year's research on hydrazine derivatives.

In 1927 he joined Triplex Safety Glass Ltd and there developed a process for mass-producing this firm's safety glass so that it could become a standard fitting in all cars and not just available by special order for luxury cars. He was also involved in the development of 'Perspex' and the 'Quick Fit' and

'Quartz' products. In 1937 he was invited to initiate the British Rubber Producers' Research Association.

In 1947, he was asked to start up the British Rayon Research Association and, again, attracted eminent scientists to work for him. These included Prof. L.R.G. Treloar, Sir George Porter FRS, Nobel Laureate, and Prof. A.S. Lodge.

On his retirement in 1957, at the age of 67 (as he said "in the prime of his life"), Mr Wilson continued for a few years his interest in applying heat treatments to various products, including textiles, by fluidized bed techniques. His major interest was, however, an attempt to develop the commercial cultivation of bamboo, initially as an indigenous source of cellulose.

Mr L.A. Wiseman, OBE

Leonard Albert Wiseman, OBE, BSc, ARIC, FTI, was born in London. After graduation at University College London, he became an assistant lecturer at King's College London, followed by a period in the Scientific Civil Service and three years (1953-56) at the UK Atomic Energy Authority, Aldermaston. He joined the British Rayon Research Association in 1956 as Deputy Director, and became its Director in January 1958. When BRRA merged with BCIRA in 1961 Mr Wiseman joined the new organization as Deputy to Dr D.W. Hill, succeeding him as Director of Research and Chief Executive of Shirley Institute in 1969.

He steered the Institute through a period of considerable change – from an organization largely concerned with the Lancashire textile industry to an outward-looking research centre with an international clientele and interests ranging beyond fibres and textiles. Mr Wiseman travelled extensively on behalf of the Institute, visiting many organizations throughout the United Kingdom and Western Europe, Australia, Sri Lanka, South Africa, Algeria, Turkey, Hong Kong, Japan, Hungary, and Czechoslovakia.

He was particularly enthusiastic about developing close links with other textile research bodies, both in the UK and overseas – notably TNO Vezelinstituut in Delft, Holland, Institut Textile de France, and the Hungarian Textile Research Institute. In the UK he was actively involved in joint committees of the Committee of Directors of Research Associations, and the Textile Research Council. In Europe he played an important role in the development of GEDRT (Groupe Européen d'Echange d'Expériences sur la Direction de la Recherche Textile). These activities were facilitated by his considerable linguistic ability, notably in French and German.

Mr Wiseman has for many years been an active member and honorary officer of the Textile Institute.

He retired from Shirley Institute on 31st October 1980.

Mr K.A. Mitchell

Managing Director of Shirley Institute, 1980-81, Kenneth A. Mitchell is an Economics graduate of Queen's University, Belfast. He is also a Fellow of the Institute of Management Consultants and a Member of the Institute of Marketing. Prior to joining the Shirley staff he had held a number of management consultancy appointments.

Dr John Honeyman

A graduate of St Andrews University, Dr Honeyman holds BSc, MA, PhD, and DSc degrees.

His first two posts were in industry, as a research chemist, at ICI Ltd and at BX Plastics Ltd. In 1945 he returned to academic life as an Assistant Lecturer at King's College London, and in 1947 he was promoted to Lecturer in Organic Chemistry, a post which he held until 1957.

Dr Honeyman's early research work was concerned with sugars, alcohols, cellulose esters and ethers, starch, and steroids. He has published (either alone or jointly) a large number of scientific papers, including a standard text-book *Introduction to the Chemistry of Carbohydrates* (1959).

Dr Honeyman came to the Institute in January 1957 as Head of the Chemistry Department, and was appointed Assistant Director in charge of chemistry and chemical processing in 1963 on the retirement of Dr A.R. Urquhart. In April 1969, Dr Honeyman's responsibilities were broadened as reflected in his new title of Assistant Director (Science and Technology).

Dr Honeyman was appointed Director of Research in 1980, at the time that Mr K.A. Mitchell became Managing Director.

He retired in October 1982.

Dr Alasdair Maclean

Dr Maclean, who is a native of the Isle of Lewis, was educated at the Nicolson Institute, Stornoway, and is a graduate of Edingburgh University. In 1963 he joined ICI Fibres Division at Harrogate, Yorks, where he served mainly in the Research Department working on process and product development of polyester filament yarns. In 1975 he was promoted to Joint Head of Research and Textile Development Department and in 1977 to the Divisional Board.

In addition to his Board responsibilities for Divisional Planning, Management Services, and a variety of commercial operations, he has also been Chairman of two ICI subsidiaries; Camtex (Fabrics) Ltd which produces nonwoven fabrics and Linear Composites Ltd a supplier of fibre-reinforced composite materials for civil engineering. He was also the ICI Division Board representative on the Boards of four overseas fibre-producers; Nurel in Spain, Finicisa in Portugal, CAFI Ltd in India, and ICI PML in Pakistan.

Dr Maclean took up his appointment as Managing Director of Shirley Institute in March 1982.